The Economics of Part-time Farming

The Economics of Part-time Farming

Ruth Gasson

THE ECONOMICS OF PART-TIME FARMING

Longman
Scientific &
Technical

Copublished in the United States with
John Wiley & Sons, Inc., New York

Longman Scientific & Technical,
Longman Group UK Limited,
Longman House, Burnt Mill, Harlow,
Essex CM20 2JE, England
and Associated Companies throughout the world.

Copublished in the United States with
John Wiley & Sons, Inc., 605 Third Avenue, New York, NY 10158

© Longman Group UK Limited 1988

First published 1988

British Library Cataloguing in Publication Data
Gasson, Ruth
    The economics of Part-time Farming.
    1. Part-time Farming – England
    I. Title
    338.1'0942   HD1476.G7
    ISBN 0-582-00550-7

Library of Congress Cataloging-in-Publication Data
Gasson, Ruth M.
    The economics of part-time farming/Ruth Gasson.
        p.   cm.
    Bibliography: p.
    Includes index.
    ISBN 0–470–21007–9 (Wiley, USA only).
    1. Part-time farming – England. 2. Farmers. Part-time – England.
3. Part-time farming – Wales. 4. Farmers, Part-time – Wales.
I. Title.
HD1930.E5G37 1988
338.1'6–dc19   87–27381
                                                                        CIP

Set in Linotron 202 10/11 pt Ehrhardt Roman
Produced by Longman Group (FE) Limited
Printed in Hong Kong

To Professor Gerald Wibberley
teacher and friend

Contents

Preface

During the mid-1960s as a junior member of the Department of Agricultural Economics at Wye College I began a study of the ways in which the growth of London was affecting farming in south-east England. Although this was originally conceived as a study of land use, I became intrigued by the social and economic changes which occurred as people from other walks of life, many from business and professional backgrounds, moved into farms. My next short but intensive contemplation of the subject dates back to 1976 when I joined four colleagues to explore in depth the meaning and implications of part-time farming. Two points impressed on my mind from that meeting were the relevance of the farm household and the need for a dynamic approach to the study of part-time farming. Following publication of the Workshop report, an international seminar was held at Wye College when discussions with researchers from a number of European countries helped to focus my ideas about the importance of part-time farming for rural and regional development. Then in the 1980s I helped to conduct a national survey of farm families with other gainful activities; data from this latest study provides much of the raw material for this book.

Up to now the farm occupier who for reasons of farm size or family circumstances, background or inclination, does not derive his income solely from farming, has tended to be dismissed as irrelevant by the agricultural policy-maker. Only recently, in view of mounting food surpluses and shrinking farm incomes and growing concern over environmental degradation and decay of rural communities, has the part-time farming option been taken seriously. Does it really offer a feasible alternative to the 'productivist' farming model or are its claims exaggerated? Will it solve the income problem on small farms? Are part-time farmers kinder to the environment than full timers? How many part-time farmers are there anyway? The aim of this book is to present the facts, to describe part-time farming as it is practised in England and Wales today with particular reference to the other occupations, sources of income, aspirations and attitudes of the families involved and to compare the situation here with trends in other industrialised countries. My hope is that this will contribute to a better informed debate and a more enlightened framing of agricultural and rural policies.

In bringing together results of fieldwork over a number of years refined by numerous discussions with colleagues in Britain and abroad, I am conscious of my debts in many directions. Gerald Wibberley first interested me in part-time farming and has remained a kind and valued adviser. Glenn Fuguitt, Tony and Heather Fuller and Gwyn Jones shared the stimulation and enjoyment of the Wye College Workshop. Allen Maunder initiated discussions with colleagues at Oxford, Exeter and Reading universities which culminated in the national survey. The original intention was to run the survey in parallel with one being conducted by the universities of Milan and Padua. The link with the Italian project is not forgotten and I should like to record my thanks especially to Danilo Agostini who organised the Bressanone seminar. The Ernest Cook Trust gave generous backing to the pilot study. I am indebted to the Ministry of Agriculture, Fisheries and Food and the Welsh Office who commissioned the farm surveys, drew the samples, advised on the nature of the enquiry, provided access to preliminary results of the Farm Structure Surveys and commented on the reports. In particular I should like to thank Aidan Power and Roger Price for their help, while emphasising of course, that the views expressed here are in no way attributable to the Ministry. Alan Harrison has made a valuable contribution by reading and commenting on many working papers and by sharing his own findings on part-time farming which strengthened confidence in my own. My colleague Berkeley Hill has given help, advice and encouragement at every stage in the survey and I am most grateful for his support. Finally I should like to thank the many part-time farmers and families pictured within. Responsibility for what is written, however, rests wholly with me.

Ruth Gasson
February 1987

Acknowledgements

Table 1.1 is adapted from The Arkleton Trust (1985, Appendix 2). Provisional results of the 1983 Labour Input Inquiry in England and Wales, kindly made available by the Ministry of Agriculture, Fisheries and Food, formed the basis for Tables 2.1, 2.2, 2.3, 3.2, 3.6, 3.7, 3.8, 4.1, 5.1, 5.9 and 7.4.

Chapter

1

The climate of opinion

There is no satisfactory way of describing the combination of farming with other gainful activities. Although widely used, 'part-time farming' is not an accurate description since it focuses on the time devoted to farming and not its combination with other work. Terms like 'multiple job holding' and 'rural pluriactivity' are gaining ground but they do not identify farming as one of the activities. 'Multiple job holding by farmers', 'multiple-occupation agriculture', 'farm families with other gainful occupations' or 'farm households engaged in rural pluriactivity' are explicit but cumbersome. For want of a better title, 'part-time farming' is used in this book to denote the combination of farming with other paid work. Farms on which it occurs are called part-time farms, and the people involved, part-time farmers, families or households. The term is always used in this general sense here. Nothing is implied about the use of time, the size of the farm or its theoretical labour requirements.

PART-TIME FARMING IN A WORLD CONTEXT

Part-time farming is an important but often neglected component in the agricultural structure of developed countries. This can be attributed partly to poor statistics, partly to the fact that it is often regarded as 'farming on the fringe' and therefore not 'real' farming (Robson 1987). Yet on the basis of information obtained from fourteen member countries the OECD (1978:2) concluded that 40 to 60 per cent of all farmers, farming couples or farm households in the world's highly industrialised countries were deriving more than half of their incomes from non-farm sources. The Arkleton Trust (1985:5) estimated that, in a fairly representative sample of sixteen market economies, more than nine million farmers, or just over half the total, were farming on a part-time basis in the 1970s. More recently the 1983 EC Farm Structure Survey found that 33 per cent of farmers in the Community had other gainful activities (Robson 1987).

Japan stands out in Table 1.1 as the country where part-time farming is predominant. The very small average size of holdings coupled with extreme immobility in the land market mean that most Japanese farm families need additional employment. Policies aimed at the harmonious development of agriculture and industry in rural areas have allowed this need to be met. In the Federal Republic of Germany, too, a policy of encouraging industrial development in marginal farming areas helps to account for the prominence of part-time farming. Mountainous terrain, a short growing season and a long-standing association between farming and other primary industries such as forestry, fishing and mining have all contributed to a high incidence of part-time farming in some Alpine and Scandinavian countries and in parts of Canada. Belgium, Italy and Spain all have large numbers of non-viable holdings and, in Spain and southern Italy in particular, many small farmers are employed on other farms. Farm structures in the United States are generally good, apart from some of the southern states. There a high level of part-time farming is attributed to highly mechanised farming systems, good transportation and plentiful job opportunities.

The UK comes low in the part-time farming league although not

Table 1.1 Importance of part-time farming in selected countries

Country	Year	Per cent part-time	Country	Year	Per cent part-time
Japan	1975	87	Sweden	1971	39
Norway	1979	69	Italy	1970	38
FR Germany	1975	55	Finland	1969	37
Austria	1973	54	Canada	1970	31
Switzerland	1975	51	Australia	1972	27
Spain	1972	48[†]	United Kingdom	1979	27
United States	1974	45	Netherlands	1975	25
Belgium	1970	43	France	1970	23
			Ireland	1972	22

(*Source*: adapted from Arkleton Trust 1985 and Tubman 1977)
† Only farmers whose main job is off the farm

at the bottom. In the 1983 Farm Structure Survey, 25 per cent of farmers in the UK and Ireland had other jobs, which is below the average for the Community of Ten but higher than in the Netherlands and Luxembourg (Robson 1987). Countries with relatively few farms run on a part-time basis seem to be characterised by highly intensive farming systems as in the Netherlands and Denmark, large farms (Australia, parts of France, England and Scotland) or a shortage of other employment opportunities (less favoured areas of France, Wales, Northern Ireland and the Irish Republic).

Part-time farming also has an important place in the centrally planned economies of eastern Europe, although its role in a collectivised agriculture is quite different from that in a free market economy. In Hungary, for example, the 1980 agricultural census listed 1.5 million part-time farms. There 40 per cent of the *total* population is engaged in part-time farming, many as members of collective farms or non-agricultural employees who also cultivate household farms (Enyedi 1982). In Poland 54 per cent of family farms had other sources of income in 1970 (Dzierwickla 1976). Most of the literature on part-time farming deals with Europe, North America and Japan. In the Third World it remains 'an unknown quantity while its true nature is still unexplored' (Christodoulou 1982).

In most of the countries included in the OECD study, part-time farms have been increasing, or at any rate disappearing more slowly than full-time farms. Within the part-time farm population, households mainly dependent on the other occupation for their livelihood have generally been increasing at the expense of those mainly dependent on farm incomes. It follows that farm families as a whole are coming to rely more on other income sources. There is every reason to expect Britain to follow the same path. Farm incomes which are increasingly unstable and falling in real terms are forcing many farmers to look hard at the alternatives. Yet little attention seems to have been paid to part-time farming in this country at the official level.

CHANGING PRIORITIES IN AGRICULTURAL POLICY

The OECD study suggested that governments' attitudes towards part-time farming depend on whether it fits in with their broad policy goals, an hypothesis which has subsequently been confirmed by Laurent (1982). Neglect of part-time farming in Britain suggests that it has been perceived as irrelevant for agricultural policy. During and after the Second World War the part-time farmer may have been dismissed as contributing little to the nation's food production. When agricultural policy entered its next phase the part-time farmer may have been regarded as a stumbling block in the drive to improve productivity, using resources wastefully and impeding progress towards an improved structure of large, full-time farms. The farmer who was only partly occupied in agriculture, partly elsewhere may have been seen as a hindrance to 'labour rationalisation', the transfer of surplus manpower from agriculture to other sectors of the economy, which was one aim of the 1965 National Plan.

Since joining the EEC Britain has been a party to the development of a more protectionist, socially oriented agricultural policy. By the mid-1980s, the Community's Common Agricultural Policy had reached a turning point. While the Community needs to pursue a price policy more adapted to the realities of the market, it is equally committed to keeping people in agriculture, with the family farm as the basic unit. In the words of the Commission's Green Paper *Perspectives for the Common Agricultural Policy*,

> In the present conditions of limited economic growth in Europe, and taking account of the ever-increasing importance of the conservation of nature and the maintenance of the fabric of rural society, there is a need to maintain a significant number of farmers on the land; the basic question is therefore whether this aim can be pursued without leading to a waste of resources and an accumulation of surpluses. (Commission 1985:3).

Part-time farming is seen as one possible solution to the problem. For one thing, it would allow families to remain on small farms at an acceptable level of income. The Green Paper argues that 'The growing importance of part-time farming with gainful outside activities corrects to some extent the overall picture of low agricultural incomes' (Commission 1985:13). The existence of appreciable non-farm earnings does not seem to have been fully taken into account in price and income support policies which are usually based on farming operations alone. The fact that some farmers derive more than half their income from non-farm sources defuses the issue of low incomes on many farms (OECD 1978:49).

Part-time farming holds out the promise of maintaining the social structure in disadvantaged rural regions. According to the Green Paper,

> In some regions, agricultural employment and activity, even if maintained by subsidies, is simply indispensable if depopulation of the countryside is to be avoided. The maintenance of a significant number of persons in agriculture is not, however, incompatible with the development – which should be encouraged – whereby a part of their income is derived from non-agricultural sources' (Commission 1985:vi).

The role of agriculture in a modern, industrial economy is seen to embrace not only strategic, economic and social functions but also the conservation of the rural environment. With the Community now self-sufficient in many farm products, environmental considerations are likely to gain in importance. Here again part-time farming may score, since it is likely to involve farming practices which are more friendly to the environment than those pursued by full-time commercial farmers.

RELEVANCE OF POLICY OBJECTIVES FOR BRITAIN

The Perspectives Green Paper was a consultative document, presenting various options for the future development of agricultural policy. It was not a statement of policy and it was not expected that the choices put forward would be equally applicable in all member states. Nevertheless the references to part-time farming do seem to find an echo in recent discussions about the future of agriculture in Britain.

Britain shares with her partners in Europe an interest in maintaining the family farm. The total number of agricultural holdings in Great Britain, which stood at over half a million at the beginning of the century, is down to a quarter of a million today. The Northfield Committee, investigating the acquisition and occupancy of agricultural land, envisaged an important and continuing role for the family farm (Northfield 1979:para 19). The National Farmers' Union, too, believes that the family farm should continue to be the basic unit and that farm policies should be directed to maintaining the viability of smaller farms (NFU 1985). Concern over decreasing numbers of small farms led to the formation of the Smallfarmers' Association in 1980, its objectives being to promote the family farm, to make farming more accessible to new entrants and to prevent the decay of rural societies. At its first conference one speaker made the point that many people, perhaps an increasing number, wish to be active on the land and derive at least a part of their living from land-based activities (Spedding 1981:28).

In the UK the long-term trend in income from agricultural activities has been downward since the early 1970s. Farm income in 1985 was the lowest in real terms for fifteen years. Prospects for recovery are not good since demand for food is, in broad terms, static or declining. Farmers may need to look to new enterprises to restore their financial position. Currently they are being encouraged to diversify into such activities as farm tourism, agricultural contracting, adding value to food products, forestry and using land, farm buildings or raw materials as a basis for light industry (Rural Voice 1985).

Diversification might help to combat the problem of declining employment in rural areas too. Numbers employed in the primary industries in rural areas – agriculture, forestry, quarrying and mining – have been falling and growth in manufacturing and service industries has not necessarily compensated. If handled the right way, part-time farming could introduce greater flexibility into situations where rural employment opportunities are limited. Wibberley (1977:124) contends that the rural areas creating the most difficult problems for planners are those where large, highly profitable farms employ very few people. Since modern agriculture is capital intensive rather than labour intensive, it needs to be complemented by other economic activities. The Country Landowners' Association maintains that the landowner has a responsibility towards rural employment. A Working Party recommended that members should consider all possibilities for creating employment, either through their own non-agricultural enterprises or by letting or selling buildings and land surplus to their own needs for the establishment of other businesses (Country Landowners' Association 1980).

The wider contributions of part-time farming to rural development are thought to be particularly important in remote, disadvantaged rural areas. Far more people are enabled to make a living in these areas than by full-time farming so that it is possible to retain the critical minimum population needed for a viable infrastructure of essential services, some of which are performed by the part-time farming families themselves (Arkleton Trust 1985:32). In the crofting counties of Scotland, for instance, the existence of a traditional small-scale and part-time farming sector stabilises the rural population even if the farming side makes an insignificant contribution to total income. Part-time farmers will travel considerable distances to and from regular employment in order to retain occupancy of their units, which they are generally reluctant to surrender. Without crofting, many of the townships currently cultivated would revert to wilderness (MacLean 1977:53–4). In the west of Ireland, too, off-farm income has helped to reduce disparities in living conditions between country and town and between small and large farms. It has improved the general living standard of farm families as indicated by ownership of consumer goods, cars and housing improvements (Cawley 1983).

In Britain, as elsewhere, public concern over threats to the environment has risen sharply in recent years, focusing on such issues as avoidance of pollution from intensive livestock production and over-use of chemicals, preservation of the landscape and less reliance on non-renewable resources. It is widely believed that the rural landscape of Britain will be better conserved on small or part-time farms, especially livestock farms, than on large, highly productive, mechanised farms. Part-time farmers are thought to have different objectives from full timers, due perhaps to the small scale of their farms, reduced dependence on farm income and possibly a greater concern for the social and environmental benefits of living in the countryside. In pursuit of their objectives, part-time farmers are less liable to become trapped on the 'technological treadmill'. Compared to other farmers they are likely to employ simpler and less intensive systems of production which are less damaging to the environment whilst at the same time exhibiting a greater willingness to invest in conservation measures. They are in a better position than their full-time counter-parts to adopt low-input farming systems which, besides being more in line with conservation aims, could make a contribution towards achieving market balance (Tracy 1984; Munton *et al.* 1985).

The pressure group Rural Voice (1985) has developed the argument that agriculture should be seen as a multi-purpose industry. Continuing support for farmers, it contends, should relate to their role as guardians of a many-sided public interest, embracing not only food production but also forestry, energy, the environment, tourism and the strengthening of the rural economy. Such an approach not only recognises that farmers may be involved in other gainful activities but positively encourages it.

While part-time farming may appear 'untidy' to some people, it obviously fulfils a very real human need. Its benefits may extend beyond the farmers and families actually involved since 'most part-time holdings can reasonably be regarded as making a valuable contribution to that variety of life which makes living in a highly industrialised society more rewarding' (Ashton and Cracknell 1961:488).

Part-time farming, then, is 'in tune with the times'. It is felt to be compatible with the aims of keeping people on the land and protecting their incomes without excessive cost to the taxpayer, of maintaining rural communities, safeguarding the environment and achieving a closer integration between agriculture and the rest of the economy.

2

Sources of information

ALTERNATIVE DEFINITIONS AND APPROACHES

Agricultural policies aimed at increasing output, improving the viability of small farms or encouraging the marginal farmer to leave the industry have tended to overlook the significance of part-time farming. So long as it was regarded as a minor side effect of structural change, it could be ignored. Now that part-time farming is being viewed in a more favourable light for its possible contribution to a broadly based strategy for rural areas, in Britain as in other developed countries, the need for information is pressing.

Statistics are collected to serve a purpose. As the overall thrust of agricultural policy has changed, so has the nature of the information which is required by policy-makers. Changes in policy ought to be reflected in the choice of definitions and methods of data collection, since information gathered to serve one set of policy objectives will not necessarily provide the most appropriate basis for developing different policies. Part-time farming illustrates the point well, having been studied from a number of angles for a variety of reasons.

In the agricultural censuses of 1907 and 1911 the occupier was 'invited to state if he did not occupy the land for business purposes or as a source of income'. The Board of Agriculture justified this enquiry in terms of interest:

> It has frequently been pointed out that the Agricultural Returns
> necessarily comprise a certain proportion of holdings which can scarcely

be regarded as being occupied for the primary object of farming as a source of profit, but may be considered rather as appanages to a residence which increase its amenities and provide occupation and interest to persons whose principal avocations lie in other directions ... it could not fail to be of interest if it were possible to differentiate the two classes, or at least to be able to form some estimate of the deduction which should be made from the total Returns in respect of those by whom the occupation of land is regarded as a matter of comparative unimportance in a pecuniary sense (Board of Agriculture and Fisheries 1907:7).

Over Great Britain as a whole nearly 6 per cent of holdings were returned as not farmed primarily for business or income in 1907. The question was not repeated after 1911 and official interest in part-time farming seems to have lapsed until the beginning of the Second World War.

The aims of the National Farm Survey, carried out in the period 1941/3, were to assist in local wartime administration, to form a permanent record of conditions on farms and to provide a basis for post-war administration, planning and policy-making. Although much of the information related to the physical layout and conditions of holdings, field recorders had to assess whether each occupier was fully engaged in farming and dependent on it for a living. On this occasion the inference may have been that a farmer with another job was not wholly committed to the food production campaign. Overall 26 per cent of farmers were found to have other sources of income and employment. The proportion of holdings of 5 acres or more not being 'farmed for business' was 5 per cent, little changed from before the First World War.

When the Small Farmers Scheme was introduced in 1959 it became necessary to identify the 'viable' small farm, capable of surviving economically and eligible for state assistance. For this purpose holdings were classified on the basis of standard man days (smd) by applying standard labour requirements to the acres of crops and numbers of livestock recorded on each holding in the agricultural census. At that time full-time work in agriculture approximated to 275 days a year, so 275 smd was taken as the dividing line between full-time and part-time holdings. Analysis of 1955 agricultural census data revealed that 180 000 of the 370 000 agricultural holdings in England and Wales were part time in this sense. When the Ministry of Agriculture conducted a survey of these part-time holdings in 1959 a large proportion of the occupiers were found to have other full-time or part-time jobs, pensions or private sources of income (Ashton and Cracknell 1961).

Ideas about part-time farming are still based to a large extent on the concept of the part-time holding, that is to say the holding which

9

is assumed to be capable of providing only part-time employment for an able-bodied adult, given average efficiency of labour. No allowance is made for circumstances on individual farms which might make it difficult to achieve average efficiency such as steep slopes, scattered fields or difficult access. The definition is based entirely on the holding under existing management; under different management by farmers with greater ability or different objectives, many of the part-time holdings could become successful full-time businesses. No account is taken, either, of what the occupier of a part-time holding actually does. He could have another job or he could simply be underemployed on the farm.

Since 1970 the agricultural census has recorded numbers of farmers under whole-time and part-time categories. On this definition, a part-time farmer is one who devotes less than full-time working or the equivalent of about forty hours a week to farm work on his holding. The 1983 agricultural census recorded 87 000 part-time and 203 000 full-time farmers, partners and directors on UK farms. There is no indication whether those farming less than full time (30 per cent of all farmers) have other paid occupations.

Defining part-time farming in terms of time spent on the farm is appropriate for policy objectives relating to labour productivity, which came to the fore during the 1960s. More recently high levels of unemployment, changing patterns of work and fears about tax evasion have induced governments to investigate the extent of moonlighting. The EC Labour Force Survey, for example, records members of the labour force with second jobs. In this context part-time farming means having a first or second job in the agricultural sector.

Since joining the EC the UK has had to furnish information on the structure of agriculture. The fundamental problems of European agriculture are felt to be essentially structural, which underlines the need for 'a dynamic socio-structural policy and effective regional and social policies'. Statistics are required to monitor the structural measures already established and to help in the development of new measures. Periodic farm-structure surveys are seen as the best way of providing comparable data which will serve as a basis for comparison between regions of the Community and between holdings (Heath 1976). The first EC structure survey was held in 1966/7, the next in 1970/1. The UK participated in the 1975, 1979/80 and 1983 surveys. The 1975 survey was the first to collect data on farmers' other gainful activities, a question subsequently extended to spouses of farmers who also worked on the farm. In the 1983 survey other gainful activities were recorded for farmers or spouses on 31 per cent of agricultural holdings in England and Wales.

Using data currently available from official censuses and surveys, then, it is possible to define part-time farming in terms of the labour requirements of the holding, use of the occupier's time or existence of another gainful activity. It is also possible to devise elaborate classifications of part-time farming by combining the three elements, which quickly run into thousands of permutations (Frank 1983; Robson 1987). Although there is a substantial degree of overlap between the three definitions, it is by no means complete. The 1975 structure survey indicated, for example, that no less than half of all UK occupiers of holdings below 275 smd worked full time on their holdings and 60 per cent of them had no other gainful activity. Conversely, a proportion of the occupiers on full-time holdings worked only part time and had other paid jobs.

Definitions of part-time farming based on the sub-viable holding or use of the occupier's time were appropriate when the main thrust of policy was to improve the productivity of resource use in agriculture. Now that the emphasis has swung more to the income and welfare needs of farm families, definitions based on the existence of other paid occupations make better sense. For present purposes the 1983 EC structure survey is the best available source of national data on part-time farming. This is not to say that it is ideal from all angles; some of its limitations will be considered in the next section.

While this discussion has concentrated on Ministry of Agriculture surveys of part-time farming linked to specific policy objectives, part-time farming has also attracted the interest of sóme agricultural economists, geographers, planners, rural sociologists and other social scientists in British universities. Inevitably these researchers have developed definitions and drawn samples to meet their particular needs, making it difficult to generalise across studies or to build on their work. The most comprehensive academic study was Harrison's 1969 survey of farm businesses in England. He found that 30 per cent of farms had at least one business principal with another source of earned income and that just over 25 per cent of all principals had other earnings (Harrison 1975:12).

For practical reasons university research has usually been confined to specific areas; for instance Thomas and Elms (1938) and later Harrison (1966) worked in Buckinghamshire, Gardner (1951) in Oxfordshire, Butler (1958) in industrial Yorkshire, Gasson (1966) in part of Kent and East Sussex, McLeay (1976) in Staffordshire, Blair (1978) in Essex. Information on part-time farming has sometimes emerged as a by-product of some other enquiry. Nalson (1968), for instance, was mainly concerned with mobility of farm families, Munton (1983) with land use in the metropolitan green belt, Davies (1969, 1971, 1973) and Bull and Wibberley (1976) with farm-based recreation and tourism.

The Agriculture Departments of Scotland and Northern Ireland have been somewhat in advance of England and Wales in monitoring part-time farming. In the late 1960s the Department of Agriculture and Fisheries for Scotland carried out a series of studies of holdings in the 'grey zone' between 100 and 350 smd. Among the topics investigated were the nature of farmers' other work, its importance relative to farming and the degree to which farm households depended on farming income (Dunn 1969). Subsequent surveys provided information on farmers' other jobs and the relative importance of farming for a random sample of Scottish farms (Wagstaff 1970; Dunn 1975). In Northern Ireland a study of small-scale beef and sheep farms assessed the sources and importance of income from off-farm employment (Moss 1980).

INFORMATION FROM THE EC STRUCTURE SURVEYS

Much of the information needed to monitor the EC farm structural measures, on crops, livestock and machinery, is routinely gathered in the UK agricultural census every year. A few questions, such as those on the legal personality of the occupier, his education and other gainful occupations, are novel and require a special survey. For the 1975 structure survey information was gathered from a sample of about 11 per cent of holdings by means of a questionnaire which was either sent by post or completed on the occasion of a farm visit by an official. In the two subsequent surveys a Labour Input Inquiry (LII) form was sent by post to a stratified 10 per cent random sample of holdings. The 1979/80 LII asked, among other things, whether the occupier and his/her spouse had another gainful occupation. The relevant question addressed to occupier and spouse in the 1983 LII was, 'As well as farm work on the holding does he or she do any other paid work?'

A total of 52 600 holdings recorded another paid job for farmer or spouse over the twelve months to June 1983. This represents 31 per cent of all agricultural holdings in England and Wales as defined for EC purposes. Various categories were, however, excluded from the survey:

(a) minor holdings, formerly known as statistically insignificant holdings, were not sampled;

(b) only those who occupied the holding as 'natural persons' were required to answer the question on other activities. This excluded some 10 000 farms run as limited companies, limited partnerships and 'other' business forms;

(c) the LII related to the agricultural holding as a physical unit and not to the farm as a business unit. A farm business may comprise several holdings;

(d) where a farm had several partners or directors, only one was recognised as 'the occupier' for the purpose of the LII;

(e) the spouse's and farmer's other paid work was only to be recorded if she or he had also worked on the holding in the previous twelve months.

A more liberal definition of part-time farming to include minor holdings, company farms, farm businesses rather than holdings, all business principals if more than one and paid work by spouses who did not work on the holding, would almost certainly have produced a larger total. The exclusion of other paid work by spouses not recorded as doing farm work was perhaps the most serious. For income and welfare purposes it is the existence of another income stream to the household which is important, not the way the farmer and spouse allocate their working time.

The definition was limited to the activities of farmers and farm-working spouses. Ideally, if the concern is the extent to which agricultural holdings provide employment and income for farm *families*, the definition should cover all working members of the farm household. The household rather than the farmer and spouse is the consumption unit, the social group with labour to deploy which is involved in making a living. A workshop on part-time farming at Wye College in 1976 favoured an all-embracing definition of part-time farming as 'the practice of a farm-based household in which one or more members are gainfully engaged in work other than, or in addition to, farming the family's holding' (CEAS 1977:7). The present definition falls well short of this comprehensive approach.

SOME FEATURES OF DISTRIBUTION

Tables 2.1 to 2.3 illustrate some features of the distribution of part-time farming. The first two show that part-time farms are predominantly small. According to Table 2.1, 40 per cent of them are below 4 European Size Units (ESU), a size of business which cannot be regarded as providing full-time work for an active occupier and which is very unlikely to yield an adequate income for a family. Most of these holdings would be below 10 hectares. A further 30 per cent are between 4 and 16 ESU, holdings which would normally be worked by the farmer alone, according to Furness (1983), although larger ones might require two persons. A further 15 per cent of part-time farms are between 16 and 40 ESU, a size to provide work for two or more persons, the remaining 15 per cent being large farms of 40 ESU or more.

Table 2.1 Distribution of part-time farms in England and Wales 1983 by size of holding in ESU†

Size of holding in ESU	Number of part-time holdings	Per cent	Part-time holdings as per cent all holdings
Under 4	21 244	40.2	48.0
4–7.9	8 914	16.9	44.8
8–15.9	7 101	13.5	32.3
16–39.9	7 744	14.7	20.1
40–99.9	5 278	10.0	15.1
100 and over	2 419	4.6	19.8
All holdings	52 700	100.0	30.7

(*Source*: provisional results of 1983 LII)
† For an explanation of these units see Glossary of terms, p. 166.

Table 2.2 gives the distribution of part-time farms by the more familiar smd-size categories. Nearly half the farms with other jobs for farmer or spouse are rated below 100 smd and 70 per cent below 250 smd, which is now the dividing line between full-time and part-time holdings. This leaves 30 per cent of the farmers and spouses with other gainful activities on holdings which should, in theory, provide full-time work for at least one person.

Part-time farming is concentrated on holdings which make only a small contribution to aggregate farm production. Holdings below 4

Table 2.2 Distribution of part-time farms in England and Wales 1983 by size of holding in smd†

Size of holding in smd	Per cent of part-time holdings	Part-time holdings as per cent all holdings
Under 100	47.2	44.9
100–249	23.2	32.7
250–499	13.5	20.5
500–999	9.6	14.1
1000 and over	6.5	13.8
All holdings	100.0	30.7

(*Source*: provisional results of 1983 LII)
† For an explanation of these units see Glossary of terms, p. 168.

ESU, a category which includes 40 per cent of all part-time farms, occupy only 8 per cent of the total crops and grass area of British agriculture and contribute less than 3 per cent of the industry's total Standard Gross Margin. At the other extreme, holdings rated at 40 ESU and above contribute more than half the total Standard Gross Margin of the industry, but only 15 per cent of part-time farms are in this size range (Furness 1983:13–15). The significance of part-time farming lies in numbers of people involved rather than in volume of production.

As a general rule the larger the farm, the less likely it is that the farmer or spouse will have other paid jobs. According to Table 2.2 the proportion of holdings where occupiers or spouses have additional jobs falls sharply with increasing farm size, tending to level out after about 1000 smd. The last column of Table 2.1 shows the proportion of holdings which are farmed on a part-time basis dropping from 48 per cent on holdings under 4 ESU to 15 per cent in the range 40 to 100 ESU. There is just a suggestion of an upturn among the very largest farms where the incidence of part-time farming rises to 20 per cent. Harrison's national survey revealed a more pronounced U-shaped distribution with part-time farming relatively more common below 20 acres (8 ha) and above 500 acres (200 ha) than in between. This could be because Harrison included, but the 1983 LII excluded, company farms and farm business principals other than the main or senior occupier. At the upper end of the farm-size spectrum it is quite likely that farming partners or directors would have other business interests, which would have the effect of accentuating the upturn in part-time farming.

The south-east region stands out in Table 2.3 as having the highest concentration of part-time farming. East Anglia and the south-west also have more than the average level, the lowest incidence occurring in Wales, the north and north-west of England. This suggests a link between part-time farming and a prosperous regional economy and more particularly with accessibility to the capital. The unique influence of London on farmers' activities has been noted before. In the 1907 agricultural census, for instance, less than 6 per cent of all holdings in Great Britain were returned as not farmed primarily for business but the proportion was over 10 per cent in Berkshire, Hampshire, Hertfordshire and Sussex, over 20 per cent in Middlesex and Surrey and 48 per cent in the London administrative area. The 1941/3 National Farm Survey, too, found high concentrations of 'occasional spare time' and 'hobby' farmers in Berkshire, Buckinghamshire, Hampshire, Oxfordshire and East Sussex. Harrison (1975) estimated that 37 per cent of all the part-time farmers in England were farming within a 60-mile radius of central London although only 23 per cent of all farms were there. Effects of other

Table 2.3 Distribution of part-time farms in England and Wales 1983 by standard region

Standard region	Number of part-time holdings	Per cent	Part-time holdings as per cent all holdings
North	3 035	5.8	27.1
Yorkshire/Humberside	4 558	8.7	29.1
East Midland	4 670	8.9	29.8
East Anglia	3 808	7.3	32.5
South-east	8 959	17.1	38.8
South-west	10 995	21.0	32.4
West Midland	5 561	10.6	30.0
North-west	3 178	6.0	26.3
Wales	7 676	14.6	26.2
All regions	52 440	100.0	30.7

(*Source*: provisional results of 1983 LII)

conurbations were less marked and did not extend so far from the centre. Harrison suggested that factors tending to drive businessmen outwards from London and into farming might carry less weight elsewhere and that appropriate residential settings might be found nearer other cities.

THE FARM SURVEYS

As the European Community's structural policy has developed, so has its need for information on structure-related topics. Practical considerations limit the number of questions which can be asked in national censuses or postal surveys. One solution is for member states to cover certain standard topics in their regular national surveys but to complement these with special surveys at intervals. This allows treatment in greater depth of items which are of particular interest at the time, with more detailed analysis at the level of the region and the individual holding (Heath 1976).

The Ministry of Agriculture commissioned Wye College to conduct special surveys of part-time farming in England and Wales along these lines. The first was intended to complement the 1979/80 structure survey, providing some broad indications of overall trends and serving as a pilot for a possible later survey. Terms of reference for the main, 1984 farm survey were

To conduct the second stage of this study in order to up-date and supplement the information gathered for England/Wales during an earlier pilot study and in the National Labour Input Inquiry which was conducted as part of the 1983 Farm Structure Survey of the European Community. In particular the study will (a) identify the nature of the main other gainful activities of farm families, (b) measure their importance to the total income of the family and (c) measure, as far as possible, the differences in (a) and (b) by region and size.

The aims of the two surveys helped to determine how the samples were drawn. Both were essentially descriptive studies, suggesting the need for a 'wide and shallow' approach, collecting a little information from a large number of subjects. An analytic study would have required a 'narrow and deep' approach with more detailed information from fewer, carefully selected cases. The most important consideration in the pilot study was to explore the whole range of situations likely to be encountered in the main survey although the second objective, of providing some indication of overall patterns, demanded a larger sample than was necessary for the exploratory function alone. The main survey, by contrast, was intended to be representative so that statements could be made with confidence about the whole of the part-time farming population. For that reason great attention had to be paid to such matters as the sampling frame, sampling fractions and weighting procedures.

The target for the pilot study was four hundred usable records, which meant approaching about six hundred individuals to allow for non-response. A number of locations was chosen throughout England and Wales with at least two in each standard region. The locations were intended to represent extremes of farming and urban influence, from upland to lowland and from urban fringe to remote rural areas with examples of intensive and extensive crop and livestock production. For each location the Ministry provided a sample of about twenty holdings from among respondents to the 1979/80 LII. These were holdings where it was reasonable to expect that farmers or members of their families would pursue some other occupation as well as farming the holding. Some had recorded another gainful activity for farmer or spouse in the LII, some were holdings where the occupier was not responsible for day-to-day management and some were holdings below the 250-smd threshold and therefore unlikely to provide a living from farming alone. The final sample of 605 holdings drawn from 34 locations yielded 427 usable records, a response rate of just over 70 per cent.

The sample for the main survey was selected from respondents who had reported another gainful activity in the 1983 LII but on this occasion, the sample had to be statistically rather than intuitively representative. The Ministry provided a random sample of 700 holdings together with a reserve sample, stratified by standard region and by size of holding. The four size bands were intended to illustrate the following situations:

1. *Main holdings below 100 smd*
   holdings judged to have some significant farming activity but small enough to be managed as spare-time enterprises;

2. *Holdings of 100 to 249 smd*
   holdings judged too small to provide full-time employment for one person or an adequate income for a family but probably too large for spare-time working;

3. *Holdings of 250 to 499 smd*
   holdings which should generate enough work to keep one person fully occupied but likely to be marginal in terms of family income needs;

4. *Holdings of 500 smd and over*
   full-time commercial holdings which should be capable of employing at least two people full time and yielding an adequate income for a family.

Occupiers of the 700 holdings in the main sample were approached and over 85 per cent agreed to cooperate in the survey. No individual region or size band achieved less than an 80 per cent response rate and the sample can therefore be regarded as reasonably representative. Where a contact was unwilling or unable to take part, a replacement was drawn from the reserve sample in the same region and size band. Since holdings had been selected at random, it was possible to raise results to national level. Most of the material presented in the following chapters was collected for the main survey. Because the sample for the pilot study was not randomly drawn, it was not possible to extrapolate from those results to the population of part-time farms with a known degree of confidence. Results of the pilot study are therefore only used where they cover ground not reworked in the main survey.

Farmers in the pilot sample were interviewed during the summer and autumn of 1981, those in the main sample in 1984. The procedures tested in the pilot were repeated with a few alterations in the main exercise. Each farmer whose name appeared in the sample was sent an initial letter explaining the purpose of the enquiry and asking him to cooperate. The letter stressed that all information disclosed would be treated in confidence, guaranteed that the interview would not take long and would be arranged at a time most convenient to the farmer and offered a summary of the findings. The letter was followed by a telephone call within a few days to arrange an interview if the farmer was willing to cooperate. Information was collected by personal interview using a structured questionnaire. Interviews normally took place on the holding and, in the main survey, lasted for about half an hour. Although the initial letter and the questions were addressed to 'the occupier' who would in most cases be the male head of household, it was often the farmer's wife who was interviewed. As most of the farms visited were family businesses, this proved to be perfectly satisfactory. In a few cases an interview was conducted with a farm secretary, manager or agent of the occupier.

The questionnaire used in the main survey collected information under the following headings:

- size, type and tenure of the holding
- size and composition of the occupier's household
- gainful occupations of all adult household members in the twelve months to June 1984
- sources of farm-household income
- non-household employees
- career history of the occupier
- future plans and objectives
- advantages and disadvantages of part-time farming
- major changes in farm organisation over the previous five years.

The pilot study had used a longer and more detailed questionnaire. Some questions were not repeated in the main survey so as to minimise demands on the farmer's time. Some of the more significant omissions related to:

- farm business form
- time devoted to each gainful activity in hours/week and weeks/year
- year of starting each activity
- occupations of farmer and spouse five years earlier
- location of off-farm employment
- details of other workers on the holding
- nature conservation on the farm
- interactions between farming and other occupations.

Respondents in the pilot study were also asked if they would allow the researchers to have access to their latest (June 1981) agricultural census form, permission being granted in 85 per cent of cases. This enabled detailed analysis to be made of the cropping and livestock on sample holdings with comparisons between various categories of part-time farm. This was felt to be a valuable exercise but was not repeated in the main survey, partly so as to minimise the burden on respondents but also because less emphasis was given in the main survey to the farming side of part-time farming. Instead more importance was attached to the activities of farm-household members and Chapter 3 turns to a consideration of the farm household.

The part-time farming family

THE FAMILY AS A UNIT OF ANALYSIS

The family has seldom been a focus for part-time farming studies, a fact which Fuller (1983) has attributed to the difficulty of aggregating census data at the family level and preoccupations with the land use and production aspects of part-time farming. Yet

> It has become increasingly clear that, in contrast to the farm, farmer and agricultural aspects that were the main emphasis of so many of the past studies of part-time farming, the farm family or household is the most useful unit of analysis. It is not the farmer alone but the family or household that decides on the use of common resources. This is the social and economic unit that allocates changing labour and other resources between farm and non-farm activities in response to perceived pressures and opportunities at home and externally. It may be seen as the interface between the farm and the non-farm environment, filtering energies, resources and ideas between them (Arkleton Trust 1985:25).

Compelling reasons for treating the farm family as the unit of analysis are that farms are rarely operated by farmers alone but usually involve the labour of other family members and that farm wives are drawn into a variety of farm tasks and decision-making activities that supplement or complement the work role of their husbands (Deseran 1984). The fact that the farm family is not a constant unit but variable in its labour resources and income needs over the course of the family cycle has particular relevance for the study of part-time farming. For policies concerned with the income and welfare of farm people, the household would seem to be a more appropriate unit than the farm business. The household approach lends itself to comparisons of total and per capita household income, parameters which would be relevant for the study of poverty. In this connection, Hill (1982) has warned of difficulties which may arise in the treatment of family members with varying degrees of financial integration with the household. While it seems logical to include the earnings of both spouses in any assessment of farm household income, it cannot be assumed that all family members who live together contribute to and share a common income. The Arkleton Trust seminar believed that all or most off-farm income is left at the disposal of the person who earns it while work on the family farm is usually recompensed by bed and board. Yet the degree to which farm youth contributes to family income has rarely been explored. In American farm families the assumption seems to be that children are an economic burden regardless of their age, valued primarily for the emotional and psychological satisfactions they provide. The fact that nearly half of all working-age children in the US are actually earning seems to have been overlooked (Deseran 1984).

The decision to operate a farm on a part-time basis depends not only on family income needs and labour resources but also on aspirations and perceptions of the alternatives. A family may choose to combine farming with some other occupation for reasons of career development, lifestyle or personal fulfilment. Coughenour and Swanson (1983) went so far as to suggest that the persistence and even growth in numbers of small farms in the United States may be directly attributable to the willingness of family members to seek off-farm employment to support a preferred life-style.

According to the Arkleton Trust,

> substantial changes are taking place, not only in the composition of the family labour-force but also in the attitudes, aspirations and roles of its individual members. Some of these changes are of a short-term nature during the course of the family and farm life-cycles. Superimposed on them, however, are longer-term changes that may substantially affect the future of part-time farming (Arkleton Trust 1985:25).

Among these longer-term changes are rising income expectations of farm families, changing attitudes to work and leisure, greater educational equality between the sexes, erosion of patriarchal and other authoritarian approaches to decision-making and their replacement by more democratic arrangements. Better educated young people are coming to attach greater value to their social independence and mobility, rejecting the role of dependent member of the family labour force. Members of farm families in Israel, for example, especially those with more education, are expressing a desire to spend part of the day away from the farm and the village and to be independent of husband and father (Regev 1980:65). In countries like Britain there is a tendency for wives on the larger and more mechanised farms to become less involved in the day-to-day work of the farm. Often with higher education and experience of off-farm work, these women are turning in increasing numbers to other careers once their children are sufficiently independent (Gasson 1984). At the same time, intensification of family work is causing new tensions, especially among female and younger members of farm households (Cavazzani and Fuller 1982).

Ideally the definition of part-time farming should encompass all gainful activities of all members of the farm household. This was the approach followed by Kada (1980) who defined a part-time farm family as 'the family in which one or more members was engaged in off-farm work, including self-employed enterprise, for basically 30 days or more during the preceding year, and thus earned off-farm income'. A full-time farming family was thus one in which no member had worked off the farm for as much as thirty days. Kada's task of comparing part-time farming families in Wisconsin, USA and Shiga Prefecture, Japan was facilitated by the fact that the Japanese agricultural census collects data on farm households.

For reasons which were explained in the last chapter, the definition of part-time farming used in the present study was largely determined by the way the question had been framed in the 1983 LII. The sample consisted of holdings with dual job farmers or spouses only. Households in which one spouse was engaged exclusively in farming and the other in non-farm work, and those where a household member other than farmer or spouse had another job, were not sampled. For each holding in the sample, however, an attempt was made to build up a complete picture of the farm household and all the gainful activities which its members had pursued during the preceding twelve months.

The all-embracing definition put forward by the Wye College workshop saw part-time farming as the practice of a farm-based *household* in which one or more members were gainfully engaged in work other than, or in addition to, farming the family's holding. The farm household was defined for purposes of the farm survey as all members normally living under the same roof as the farmer and sharing common housekeeping, in the twelve months to June 1984. According to this definition children away at boarding school or college should have been excluded on the grounds that they had spent fewer than half the nights in the year at home. By the same token non-related persons living in the farmhouse, such as domestic help or resident students, should have been included. In the event only twelve of the seven hundred households visited were found to include members not related to the farmer by kinship or marriage and usually these persons were long-standing family friends or partners in the farm business. For all practical purposes, then, the farm household can be taken to mean all members of the farmer's family currently living at home. From now on the terms 'family' and 'household' are used interchangeably.

CHARACTERISTICS OF PART-TIME FARMERS

Since the farm household was defined in relation to the farmer, one of the first tasks of the farm survey was to identify 'the farmer'. He or she is the person legally responsible for all financial and economic risks in the farm business. Where two or more persons shared this responsibility it was necessary to identify the 'principal' farmer, the one ultimately responsible for decisions about investment and allocation of capital. In cases where it was impossible to decide who was the principal farmer, questions were directed to the senior partner and his household.

The farmer identified in the 1984 farm survey was not always the occupier who had completed the 1983 LII form for the holding. The lapse of a year inevitably brought a few changes through death, illness, retirement, removal and marital breakdown. Examples occurred of a dual-job farmer retiring in favour of a son who was farming full-time and of a couple separating where the spouse with the second job had left the family and the farm. Some farmers and spouses had given up their other jobs between 1982/3 and 1983/4 which helps to explain why a small number of the holdings visited (31) were not being farmed on a part-time basis in 1984.

In cases of family partnerships where it was difficult to identify the principal farmer, the farm survey could produce a different result from the 1983 LII. As interviews were frequently conducted with the wife in the husband's absence, there may have been a tendency to treat the wife as principal farmer although the husband would probably have been identified as the farmer on an official form. This may help to explain why the proportion of female occupiers of part-time farms, which was estimated in both the main farm survey and the pilot to be 13 per cent, was higher than the 8 per cent reported in the 1983 LII. While this would have some consequences for the characteristics of farmers which are described below, it would not have affected the selection of the sample nor the overall composition of the households and their activities.

Women may be better represented among part-time than full-time farmers because part-time holdings are predominantly small and women generally farm on a smaller scale than men. A national survey of the farm labour force in 1970 found that the average size of farms run by men was 162 acres (66 ha) while women's farms averaged only

84 acres (34 ha) (Gasson 1980a:19). The 1975 structure survey recorded female occupiers on 10 per cent of holdings below 275 smd but only on 3 per cent of those rated at 275 smd and over. In the farm survey, women were sole or principal occupiers of 17 per cent of part-time farms in size band 1 but only 4 per cent in band 4.

Female farmers tend to be concentrated in southern England and in the pastoral west and Wales with fewer in the eastern arable or northern regions (Gasson 1980a). This holds true for part-time farming as well. The farm survey did not find any female occupiers among part-time farmers in the Yorkshire/Humberside region and very few in the north or East Midland regions. Yet in the north-west of England and Wales more than one fifth of the part-time farmers were women.

According to the farm survey 87 per cent of part-time farmers in England and Wales are married. This figure is in line with the population census and other surveys which have found that between 80 and 90 per cent of all farmers in England and Wales are married (see, for example, Agriculture EDC 1972; Harrison 1975; Newby *et al.* 1978). The proportion of part-time farmers who were married was higher than might have been expected from a sample of predominantly *small* farms. The Agriculture EDC study, for instance, showed the proportion of farmers who were married rising steadily from under 77 per cent on farms which employed no workers to 89 per cent on farms with 5 or more regular workers. The present result was, however, confirmed by the pilot study and by three studies in various parts of Ireland which found higher proportions of part-time than full-time farmers married (Curry 1972; Moss 1980; Higgins 1983). The vicious circle which links small farms and poor living conditions with celibacy and demographic wastage has been graphically described by Nalson (1968). Where the farm business is too small to support two families and the farmhouse too cramped to accommodate them, the potential successor may have to choose between farm inheritance and marriage. The son who postpones marriage until he controls the farm risks remaining single or, if he marries a woman of his own age, childless. This syndrome is most characteristic of small *full-time* farms, however. In rural areas where other jobs are available, farmers' sons may be able to combine other employment with work on the home farm. By this means they can afford to marry at an early age without jeopardising their chances of taking over the farm eventually. Part-time farming would subsequently allow a young couple to raise a family on a farm which was below the margin of viability. Therefore there is no reason to expect a high proportion of unmarried *part-time* farmers on small farms.

Male farmers are more likely than females to be married and this seems to hold for part-time and full-time alike. Here it has to be

Table 3.1 Marital status of male and female part-time farmers in England and Wales

Sex of farmer	Married	Not married	All farmers	Per cent single
		estimated numbers		
Male	41 786	3 700	45 486	8.1
Female	3 844	3 014	6 858	44.0
All farmers	45 630	6 714	52 344	12.8

(*Source*: 1984 farm survey, raised results)

remembered that some women only become farmers through the death of their husbands. According to the farm survey 92 per cent of male but only 56 per cent of female part-time farmers were currently married. (The 1971 population census recorded 59 per cent of female farmers as married.) As Table 3.1 shows, the small band of female part-time farmers in the survey accounted for nearly half the total who were single, widowed or divorced. This seems to suggest that factors which make it difficult for a woman to combine farming with marriage, with its implied responsibilities for child care and housekeeping, operate in part-time as much as in full-time farming. Having another job would in fact impose an additional load on the woman. In short, part-time farming and marriage may be positively associated for men but negatively associated for women.

The OECD series of studies concluded that farmers who have other jobs are, on average, younger than those without, an observation recently confirmed by studies in Poland (Kłodziński 1983), Sweden (Persson 1983) and western Ireland (Cawley 1983). Striking differences were found in the Irish Republic where only 24 per cent of part-time farmers but 43 per cent of all landholders were aged 55 or over (Higgins 1983:40). A Louisiana study established that farm couples where neither worked off the farm tended to be the oldest, those with only the farmer working off the farm in between and those with the wife working off, the youngest (Deseran 1985). Similar results were obtained in a study of farm families in New York State (Buttel and Gillespie 1984)

Part-time farmers in England and Wales, too, tend to be younger than full timers. According to Table 3.2 40 per cent of farmers with other jobs but only 23 per cent of those without are aged under 45. Full-time farmers are more than three times as likely as part timers to be aged 65 and over. Most of the earlier studies reached the conclusion that the population of part-time farmers was older than

Table 3.2 Age distribution of farmers with and without other jobs in England and Wales 1983

Age range	Farmers with other jobs	Farmers without other jobs
	per cent of farmers	
Under 35	10.7	6.4
35–44	29.4	16.6
45–54	31.4	24.8
55–64	21.7	28.6
65 and over	6.8	23.6
All farmers	100.0	100.0

(*Source*: provisional results of 1983 LII)

the farming population at large. This is because they based their definitions of part-time farming on the small or sub-viable holding and such holdings tend to be more important for people at the end of their careers. Ashton and Cracknell (1961) for instance found that more than 28 per cent of occupiers on holdings below 275 smd were over 60 as against 20 per cent of all farmers in the 1951 population census. In Scotland the number of occupiers aged 65 and over on holdings below 100 smd was roughly double that on farms of 250 smd and above (Wagstaff 1970; Rettie 1975).

THE FARM-FAMILY CYCLE

The pattern of family activities varies according to stage in the family cycle. Nalson (1968:54) divided the cycle into three stages which he related to changing labour resources and income needs of the family.

(a) An *early* stage up to the time when the first child leaves school. Physical and financial pressures on the family are likely to be heavy at this time with demands of growing children competing with the need to establish the farm business. Usually husband and wife are the only household members available for employment on or off the farm but the wife may be prevented from working by childbearing and rearing.

(b) A *middle* phase beginning when the first child starts work and ending when all children have left home. At this time family consumption needs are at a peak but more family members are available for employment. If the farm cannot absorb all the labour available one or more members will seek work elsewhere. Part-time farming is there-fore likely to occur at this stage.

(c) A *late* phase from the time the last child leaves home until the couple retires or dies. Household consumption needs are diminished but so is the capacity of the farmer and wife to cope with farm work. They may cut down on activities off the farm or they may decide to put less effort into farming. Part-time farming is less likely to occur at this time.

Real life does not fit into such neat categories. Nalson found, for instance, that the 'empty nest' stage did not always occur on large farms capable of supporting more than one household as sons could marry and continue to work on the farm. He also identified incomplete families where, for one reason or another, the family cycle was destined to be broken. Two further categories were added in order to accommodate all the household types encountered in the farm survey:

(d) Households including one or more members of the *parental generation*. This could mean that the farmer was single and living with parents or that the farmer and his family shared their home with one or more of the grandparents.

(e) Incomplete families including farmers who were unmarried and living alone and one-parent families.

The OECD study suggested that part-time farming would be most prevalent in the early phase of the family cycle:

> Frequently, farmers first undertake off-farm work to see them through certain stages in their family or farm life cycle ... The off-farm work is frequently undertaken to pay off mortgage debt on the farm, to buy new machinery or to stock the farm, to buy equipment for the farmhouse, to cover the high costs incurred in rearing a family and so on (OECD 1978:15).

The farm survey estimated that 42 per cent of part-time farming families in England and Wales were at the early stage, before any child had completed full-time education and entered the labour force (Table 3.3). The corresponding figure for the pilot study was 44 per cent. This seems to support the suggestion made in the OECD study although no comparable data are available on the life-cycle stages of full-time farming families in this country. A greater proportion of families in the middle stage with children in employment, might have been anticipated. Here it has to be remembered that the sample was drawn from holdings with farmer and/or spouse working; households with members other than farmer or spouse in employment were not sampled.

No association was found between stages in the family cycle and farm size but the survey revealed highly significant regional differences.

Table 3.3 Numbers of part-time farming families in England and Wales by stage in the family cycle

Stage in cycle	Estimated number of families	Per cent
(a) Early	22 130 *a*†	42.2
(b) Middle	12 404 *b*	23.7
(c) Empty nest	9 106 *b*	17.4
(d) Parental generation	4 220 *c*	8.1
(e) Incomplete	4 485 *c*	8.6
All families	52 344	100.0

(*Source*: 1984 farm survey, raised results)
† For an explanation of these symbols, see Statistical tests, p. 169.

As Table 3.4 shows, the early phase of family development is well represented among part-time farming families in the north of England, Yorkshire/Humberside and Wales but poorly represented in East Anglia, which has by far the largest proportion of households in the empty-nest stage. Families in the middle phase with children earning are most prevalent in Yorkshire/Humberside, the north-west and East Midlands. Moving south and east the proportion of incom-

Table 3.4 Distribution of part-time farming families by stage in the family cycle and region

Region	a	b	c	d	e	All households
	per cent of households					
North	50.7	18.5	24.6	1.3	4.0	100.0
Yorks/Humber	50.2	37.5	9.2	3.1	0.0	100.0
E. Midland	41.8	32.3	8.1	5.5	12.3	100.0
East Anglia	29.4	17.9	35.6	6.7	10.4	100.0
South-east	40.5	21.3	20.6	5.2	12.4	100.0
South-west	39.5	21.5	18.6	9.4	11.0	100.0
W. Midland	42.1	21.4	19.2	12.0	5.3	100.0
North-west	34.8	36.6	17.9	4.8	5.9	100.0
Wales	50.4	17.2	9.1	15.8	7.5	100.0
All regions	42.2	23.7	17.4	8.1	8.6	100.0****†

(*Source*: 1984 farm survey, raised results)
† For an explanation of this symbol, see Statistical tests, pp. 169–70.

plete families increases. Households in Wales, the West Midlands and the south-west are the most likely to include one or both of the farmer's or spouse's parents.

These findings are open to various interpretations. One possibility is that cultural differences between north and south are reflected in family structures. Farm families in the north of England and in Wales might be depicted as tending towards the extended type and more cohesive than in the south. This might account for parents remaining in the farmhouse when children take over the running of the farm, for more young families being found on farms and for children continuing to live at home after starting work. The nuclear family or one-generation household might be more prevalent in the south and east, meaning that young people would leave home when they entered the labour force and that parents would be disinclined, or discouraged, from living in the farmhouse after they retired.

The explanation might lie in different economic opportunities between regions. Farmers' children in the north of England and the Midlands might be obliged to continue living at home after leaving school because they cannot find jobs which pay well enough to allow them to live independently. A combination of low farm incomes and high prices for rural property might be preventing older farmers in Wales, the south-west and West Midlands from buying retirement homes, which would help to account for the high incidence of three generation households in those regions.

Another line of reasoning would be that there are regional differences in the backgrounds of part-time farmers and their route into farming. Previous research has shown that many part-time farmers in the Home Counties enter the industry relatively late in life, having already established themselves in other careers. Their parents would probably have died by this stage and their children embarked on careers of their own, so the farm would never have functioned as the family home. In the north of England it may be more usual for the farm to be handed down within the family. This would help to explain why there are relatively more children and parents of farmers on part-time farms in the north. The farm survey was not designed to test these hypotheses, which must remain conjectural, but Chapter 8 provides some support for the last suggestion.

SIZE OF PART-TIME FARMING HOUSEHOLDS

Despite evidence of some regional differences, the nuclear family is the norm for part-time farming households. According to the farm survey the modal household has four members, usually a couple with two children. Only one household in six has more than four members and only one in twenty consist of the farmer alone. There is little here to support the suggestion from the OECD and Polish studies that part-time farmers have larger families than other farmers.

On the basis of the farm survey it is estimated that part-time farms in England and Wales provide a labour force of some 114 000 persons, including some who work only on the family farm, an average of 2.2 workers per household. More than half the households have just two members, usually the farmer and spouse, in employment. Only a quarter have more than two breadwinners.

The larger the farm, the larger the workforce. Table 3.5 shows a significant association between size of holding and number of household members in gainful employment, although not all members would necessarily work on the farm. Only 23 per cent of holdings in band 1 have more than two household members in work compared with 34 per cent in band 4. The smallest holdings are the most likely to have only one breadwinner. One reason why larger farms tend to support larger families is that children do not leave home. Where the farm requires more labour than husband and wife can provide, one child may be prevailed upon to stay at home and work for the parents with the prospect of taking over the farm eventually (Nalson 1968:53).

The number of family members in work also varies significantly by region. Yorkshire and Humberside, the north-west and the East Midlands are the regions most likely to have more than two household members in employment while south-east England and Wales have the most households in which only the farmer is available for work. As Table 3.4 showed, the first three were the regions with the most families in the middle stage of the family cycle while the south-east had the highest number of incomplete families.

Table 3.5 Size of household labour force by size of holding

| Size band | Number of persons per household gainfully employed | | | |
	one	two	more than two	all households
	per cent of part-time farming households			
1	19.7	57.6	22.7	100.0
2	10.0	64.6	25.4	100.0
3	11.3	57.9	30.8	100.0
4	14.4	52.0	33.6	100.0
All holdings	16.0	58.1	25.9	100.0 **

(*Source*: 1984 farm surveys, raised results)

ALLOCATION OF WORK ROLES WITHIN THE HOUSEHOLD

The 31 per cent of holdings in England and Wales recording another job for farmer or spouse in the 1983 LII can be broken down to 20 per cent where the farmer only has another job, 5 per cent for the spouse only and 6 per cent for both. In addition 8 per cent of holdings recorded other paid work for other members of the farm family but the extent of overlap between that 8 per cent and the 31 per cent is not known.

The way work is shared among members of the farm household varies according to the size of the farm. Table 3.6 shows the proportion of holdings where the farmer only has another job declining rapidly with increasing size of farm business, with just a hint of an upturn when the very large sizes are reached. The likelihood of both farmer and spouse having other jobs drops even more rapidly with increasing farm size. For spouses and other family members the relationship with farm size is weaker but in the opposite direction, rising to a maximum on middle-sized farms and then decreasing again.

This pattern is logical, assuming that it is the farmer who has first responsibility for the farm work. On very small holdings the farmer would probably be able to cope with all the farm work on his own as well as his off-farm job, without having to involve other members of the family. With increasing size of farm some help is needed so spouses and other members of the family are drawn in to help but

Table 3.6 Distribution of other gainful activities in part-time farming families by position in family and size of holding

Size of holding in ESU	Per cent of holdings reporting another job for:			
	farmer only	farmer and spouse	spouse only	other members
Under 4	33.1	10.4	4.3	9.6
4–7.9	30.7	8.6	5.6	11.5
8–15.9	21.1	5.7	5.5	10.3
16–39.9	10.8	2.9	6.3	8.3
40–99.9	7.8	2.2	5.1	7.0
100 and over	12.8	2.7	4.3	5.1
All holdings	19.7	5.7	5.2	8.6

(*Source*: provisional results of 1983 LII)

as this is not likely to provide them with full-time employment, they may combine it with other activities. On larger farms where employment of non-family labour can be justified, it would not be necessary for the farmer's wife or children to help on the farm if they wished to pursue other careers.

Data from the farm survey showed that whatever the size of holding, more farmers than spouses have second jobs but spouses' other jobs are relatively more important on larger farms. In Wisconsin, too, the wife was the only dual-job holder on 2 per cent of part-time farms below 100 acres (40 ha) but on 19 per cent above 200 acres (80 ha) (Kada 1980:100). As Buttel observed for the United States, 'the substantial inverse relationship between farm size and off-farm labour market participation by male farm operators does not hold with regard to farm women' (Buttel 1982:299). Larger farms which generate enough work to keep the farmer fully occupied ought to provide an adequate income for a family, so off-farm work for the wife might be regarded as an expression of choice rather than of necessity (Gasson 1984). The fact that many operators of larger farms marry women from non-farm backgrounds, often with higher and professional qualifications, helps to explain why it is often wives rather than husbands on the larger farms who have off-farm jobs (Symes and Marsden 1983). Bouquet (1985) has argued persuasively that wives who are excluded from farm-production activities on larger farms need to become involved in other activities in order to maintain their status within the farm family. In the remote Devon coastal parish which she studied the main options for farmers' wives were taking in visitors and becoming involved in good causes but in more accessible areas the woman's choice may be extended to include off-farm work. Sander (1983) notes that farmwives in the United States are improving their status in the farm-family economy through off-farm work.

More than three-quarters of all farmers in part-time farming households are themselves dual job holders combining at least one other gainful activity with farming. Several farmers interviewed in the survey were found to be coping with no less than five jobs at the same time! Farm size was an important influence here, the proportion of dual job holders falling from 85 per cent in band 1 to 66 per cent in band 4.

According to the survey 40 per cent of farmers in part-time farming families are married to spouses who are dual-job holders and 36 per cent have spouses with one gainful activity. This leaves 24 per cent of farmers who are either unmarried or whose wives are full-time housewives. Although work on the family's holding counts as a gainful activity even if the person is not paid for it, the work of keeping house and caring for children is not. Since most spouses were also house-

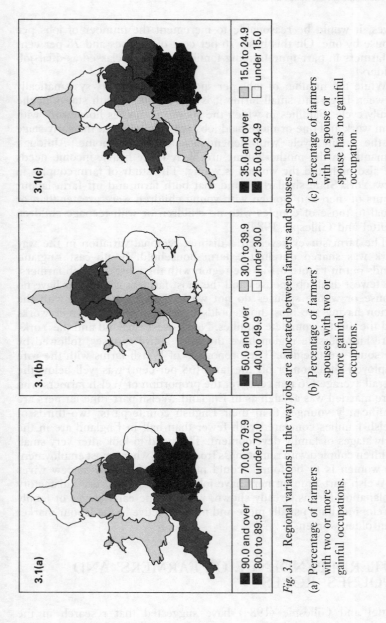

Fig. 3.1 Regional variations in the way jobs are allocated between farmers and spouses.

(a) Percentage of farmers with two or more gainful occupations.

| 90.0 and over |
| 80.0 to 89.9 |
| 70.0 to 79.9 |
| under 70.0 |

(b) Percentage of farmers' spouses with two or more gainful occupations.

| 50.0 and over |
| 40.0 to 49.9 |
| 30.0 to 39.9 |
| under 30.0 |

(c) Percentage of farmers with no spouse or spouse has no gainful occupation.

| 35.0 and over |
| 25.0 to 34.9 |
| 15.0 to 24.9 |
| under 15.0 |

wives, it would be reasonable to increment the number of jobs per spouse by one. On this basis 76 per cent of spouses and 78 per cent of farmers in part-time farming families could be classed as dual-job holders.

While the number of jobs per spouse does not vary systematically between large and small farms it is closely linked with stages in the family cycle. Families in which the spouse combines housework with farm work and one or more paid jobs are most often in the early stage of the family cycle with dependent children at home. Although demands on the mother's time are likely to be heavy, income needs are also high and the woman is young. The study of farm couples in New York State similarly found that both farm and off-farm labour inputs of men and women with young children were greater than or equal to those of couples with no children or with teenage children (Buttel and Gillespie 1984).

The farm survey revealed a distinct regional variation in the way work was shared out in the farm household. South-east England stands out in Figure 3.1 as the region with the most dual-job farmers, the fewest dual job spouses and the most farmers who either have no spouse or whose spouses do not work. This is consistent with the region having the most households in which only the farmer works and the most incomplete families. North-west England and the Yorkshire/Humberside region have the most active spouses, followed by the south-west region. The proportion of Welsh farms with the wife employed either on or off the farm (68 per cent) was well below the overall average (76 per cent) yet the proportion of Welsh farmers who were married was as high as in England. Welsh part-time farmers are significantly younger than their English counterparts; two-thirds of Welsh families compared with fewer than half in England are in the early stages of family development. The need to look after very small children coupled with remoteness from towns, where most employment for women is to be found, could help to explain why so few wives of Welsh part-time farmers have jobs. This is not a very satisfactory explanation for, as already shown, wives in the early stages of family development are usually more and not less active in the labour market than older women.

INTERDEPENDENCE OF FARMERS' AND SPOUSES' ROLES

Buttel and Gillespie (1984) have suggested that research in the sociology of agriculture has not yet come to grips with the way family labour is allocated on and of the farm and with the interdependence of work roles, Kada's study being a notable exception. Recent studies on the roles of farm women, for instance, have tended to concentrate on farm work, neglecting to explain how women's work on the farm is related to their off-farm work or to the farm and off-farm work of men. Continuing emphasis on the farm business rather than the farm household is blamed for this omission.

It would not be surprising to find an inverse relationship between the amount of farm work performed by farmers and other members of the household in part-time farming families. Most of the evidence seems to point the other way, however. Both Kada and Buttel and Gillespie found positive correlations between farmers' and spouses' labour inputs on US farms. Some information gleaned from the 1983 LII leads to the same conclusion. The proportion of full-time and part-time farmers reporting that their spouses had worked on the holding in the previous twelve months was virtually the same. As Table 3.7 shows, part-time farmers were more likely than full timers to be helped by their spouses on small, family-worked farms of less than 16 ESU, but above about 20 ESU, a size of business where hired labour might be justified, it was the full-time farmers who were more likely to report that their spouses had done farm work. This

Table 3.7 Spouses' farm work on part-time farms by farmers' activities and size of holding

Size of holding in ESU	Farmer has another job	Farmer has no other job
	per cent with spouses doing farm work	
Under 4	46.7	30.2
4–7.9	51.1	41.0
8–15.9	53.5	48.9
16–39.9	56.8	59.5
40–99.9	56.0	61.7
100 and over	47.7	58.1
All holdings	50.4	51.1

(*Source*: provisional results of 1983 LII)

seems to suggest a degree of labour substitution with wives standing in for absent husbands on smaller farms. On larger, labour employing farms that role is presumably taken over by a farm manager or foreman.

By the same token, some substitution between farmers' and spouses' off-farm work might be expected; if one spouse works off the farm the other will have greater responsibility for farm work and will therefore be less likely to work elsewhere. In fact the 1983 LII suggested

Table 3.8 Spouses' and farmers' other activities by size of holding

Size of holding in ESU	Farmer has another job	Farmer has no other job
	per cent with spouses who have other jobs	
Under 4	23.9	7.7
4–7.9	21.9	9.2
8–15.9	21.4	7.5
16–39.9	21.2	7.3
40–99.9	21.8	5.7
100 and over	17.2	5.1
All holdings	22.4	7.0

(*Source*: provisional results of 1983 LII)

the opposite. Farmers with other jobs are three times as likely as full-time farmers to have spouses with other jobs and, as Table 3.8 shows, this effect is independent of farm size. A study of American farm women similarly found a positive and significant association between off-farm employment of husbands and wives (Jones and Rosenfeld 1981:49–50). Buttel and Gillespie, too, found a modest positive association which was independent of farm size. The association between off-farm work by farmers and wives in the pilot study was also positive and highly significant. This surprising result runs counter to what might be expected on common-sense grounds. It also conflicts with the discovery that for the EC as a whole and over each sector of the economy, high rates of double jobholding by males are associated with low rates of labour-force participation by females (Alden and Spooner 1981:69)

A possible explanation might lie in different perceptions of women's work as between full-time and part-time farmers. The norm in Britain today is for wives to work outside the home and for their work in any sphere to be recognised. This may be less true in agricultural circles than elsewhere. Among larger farms, at least, there still appears to be a lingering element of prejudice against wives being regularly involved in farm work or employed off the farm (Gasson 1980b:xv). There is some evidence that farmers underestimate the work that their wives do on the farm (see for instance Jones and Rosenfeld 1981:24–5). It is possible, too, that some farmers take 'farm work' to mean physical work, ignoring the increasingly important clerical, secretarial and administrative functions which are often the province of their wives.

At a perceptual level it is possible that attitudes towards women's work might have affected the way the LII form was completed. It will be recalled that in the 1983 LII any paid work by the spouse was only to be recorded if the spouse had also done farm work in the past year. A farmer who subscribed to more 'traditional' values, whose wife pursued some occupation off the farm, might discount any contribution she made to farm work and would therefore not record her as having another paid job. A part-time farmer from a different background with a more 'modern' attitude towards women's work, on the other hand, would be more inclined to give full value to his wife's activities both on and off the farm when filling in such a form. This might help to account for the strong association between off-farm work of farmers and off-farm work of spouses as revealed in the 1983 LII. It is stressed, however, that this explanation is highly tentative and it does not account for similar results being obtained in the United States. Such an intriguing puzzle demands further study but meanwhile, Chapter 4 returns to the more straightforward topic of work on the part-time farm.

Work on the family farm

Although use of time has been superseded as the main criterion for defining part-time farming for reasons which were discussed in Chapter 2, it remains an important variable. The more time is devoted to other work, the less is available for the farm. Over the long term the way farming families allocate their time between competing activities indicates how much importance is attached to farming. In the shorter term, pressures which arise from trying to combine two jobs and the degree of success in coping with them may determine whether a family continues in farming or quits. The kinds of adjustment that are made in order that part-time farming may be possible, such as substituting labour within the family, employing non-family labour, exchanging help with neighbours, altering the scale and system of farming or tailoring the off-farm job to the demands of the farm, all help to give part-time farming its distinctive flavour. This chapter therefore begins by considering the amount of time farmers expend on their holdings and the nature of their contributions.

TIME WORKED BY FARMERS

Table 4.1 measures the time occupiers work on their holdings against the yardstick of a year's work by a full-time farm worker. Farming and other activities are clearly very competitive. Over half of all part-time farmers and 84 per cent of those with another job as their main activity had worked less than half time on their holdings in the

Table 4.1 Time farmers work on their holdings by existence of other jobs

Time worked as per cent full-time working	Farmers with other paid jobs			Farmers without other jobs
	major	minor	any	
		per cent of farmers		
Under 50	84.0	14.0	56.9	16.9
50–99	11.3	47.0	25.1	7.0
100	4.7	39.0	18.0	76.1
All farmers	100.0	100.0	100.0	100.0

(*Source*: provisional results of 1983 LII)

previous twelve months while over three-quarters of those without other jobs had worked on the farm full time.

The farm survey estimated that 40 per cent of all occupiers of part-time farms had worked full time on the holding in 1983/4, including some who had no other jobs. Full-time working was defined as at least 35 hours a week throughout the year, part-time being less than 35 hours on average but on a regular basis, working for some time in every month of the year. It was estimated that 51 per cent of occupiers had worked part time, 5 per cent on an occasional basis and 4 per cent not at all. The amount of time the farmer spends in farm work is closely linked to the size of the holding. In the top size band 74 per cent of farmers had worked full time, in the lowest only 22 per cent. Part-time working seems to be especially important on the smallest holdings and it is here, too, that farmers are most likely to do no regular work on the farm. Table 4.2 gives just a hint that farmers in the top size band are more inclined than those in the middle bands to do no regular farm work, a relationship which was more pronounced in the pilot study.

The time farmers spend on their holdings varies significantly by region, south-east England and the East Midlands having the fewest who work full time. It also varies significantly over the course of the family cycle, full-time working most often being associated with large, three-generation households and with the middle stage of the cycle. It may be that if there are more household members in employment the farmer can devote more of his time to the farm or it may be that larger households are associated with larger holdings where the farmer is likely to be fully employed (see Table 3.5).

More detailed information about the amount of time devoted to farm and other work was collected in the pilot study. Farmers in that sample averaged about 30 hours a week on their farms throughout

Table 4.2 Time farmers worked on part-time holdings in 1983/4 by size of holding

	Full-time	Part-time	Occasional/none	All farmers
Size band	per cent of part-time farmers			
1	21.8	66.0	12.2	100.0
2	47.9	47.8	4.3	100.0
3	62.6	33.1	4.3	100.0
4	74.2	17.3	8.5	100.0
All holdings	39.8	51.0	9.2	100.0 ***
Estimated numbers	20 821 *a*	26 705 *a*	4 818	52 344

(*Source*: 1984 farm survey, raised results)

the year, spouses who did any farm work 16 hours, other family workers 30 hours and hired workers 38 hours. The distribution of hours worked by regular employees was very close to that for all hired men on farms in England and Wales at the time. The figure for spouses, too, was only slightly below the 17 hours per week for working wives on full-time farms which was recorded in the 1970 survey of the farm labour force in England and Wales (Agriculture EDC 1972: 39–41). The biggest difference was in respect of farmers' hours. According to the Agriculture EDC study full-time farmers worked the longest hours of all, nearly half of them maintaining that they put in at least 70 hours a week. Only 8 per cent of part-time farmers in the pilot study spent as long on their holdings. The average for full-time farmers was 64 hours compared with 30 hours for part timers in the pilot study.

Adding on the hours devoted to the second job brings part-time farmers back towards the level of full timers. Those farmers with other agricultural or farm-based employment averaged another 20 to 25 hours a week. Those with off-farm employment were usually more heavily committed, averaging 35 hours a week in the other job. This does not include time spent travelling between the farm and the other place of work. Dual-job holding may therefore amount to 50 to 70 hours of work a week which represents very full use of the farmer's time. Part-time farmers in Ireland similarly averaged 50 hours a week on and off the farm, those with full-time off-farm jobs working particularly long hours (Higgins 1983: 61).

Reviewing the literature on part-time farming Martens (1980) concluded that most part-time farmers probably have to work harder and longer than they would without the other job even after making adjustments towards more extensive systems of farming. Raising household income may only be achieved at the price of less leisure time for the farmer and spouse. As Hanf and Müller (1974/5) have demonstrated, moving from full-time to part-time farming usually means less labour being allocated to the farm but also a reduction in leisure for farmer and wife. In extreme cases this might lead to family conflict or a breakdown of the farmer's health. In the Irish study Higgins (1983:71–2) found that while the majority of part-time farmers were satisfied with their working arrangements a minority were finding it difficult to cope because of the number of hours they were obliged to work. In the present study, too, stress from trying to combine two jobs was the main disadvantage mentioned by part-time farmers. This topic will be raised again in Chapter 9.

THE NATURE OF FARMERS' CONTRIBUTIONS

Although many part-time farmers are absent from their holdings for much of the working day they continue to exercise responsibility for the day-to-day management of the business. Three out of four part-time farmers, according to the farm survey, are entirely responsible for the running of their holdings. Half the remaining occupiers share responsibility on an informal basis with others and the rest delegate it to someone else. The other person involved is usually a member of the household but it could be a partner or relative living nearby, a neighbouring farmer, a contractor, a tenant, an agent or an employed manager. In fact very few part-time farmers employ professional farm managers, the estimate being only 1300 or under 3 per cent of all part-time farms in England and Wales.

Larger holdings are usually managed by the farmer alone but if this is not possible, by an agent or employed manager. It is on the smaller holdings where the farmer is more likely to have another full-time job, that responsibility is more often shared on an informal basis with other family members or neighbours. Some of these holdings are very small indeed and few decisions would need to be taken from one week to the next.

Most farmers, then, take full responsibility for the day-to-day running of their holdings and work there on a regular if not a full-time basis. Generally some help is forthcoming from spouses or other members of the family but only a minority of part-time farmers employs non-family labour on a regular basis. This means that the farmer is usually the mainstay of the labour force, fully involved in everything that needs to be done. Over 80 per cent of part-time farmers interviewed in both the pilot and main surveys said that they tackled every

Table 4.3 Type of work performed by part-time farmers by size of holding

Type of farm work	Size band 1	2	3	4
	per cent of holdings			
Anything needed	85.2	86.8	85.3	80.2
Managerial only	4.0	2.9	6.8	12.2
Specified manual tasks	5.1	5.7	3.4	2.4
No work/not known	5.7	4.6	4.5	5.2
All farmers	100.0	100.0	100.0	100.0 **

(*Source*: 1984 farm survey, sample results)

kind of farm task that cropped up, with or without help. A small minority supervised the business side without doing any manual work themselves and Table 4.3 suggests that this was more typical of the larger farms. A few part-time farmers confined their activities to certain tasks such as haymaking, fencing, repairing machinery or maintaining buildings. Some who let the land on grazing tenancies were only responsible for fencing and draining it; this was more likely to occur on smaller holdings.

FARM WORK BY SPOUSES

One question which this chapter tries to address is whether part-time farmers make any attempt to compensate for their absence from the holding by involving their spouses or other members of the family more in farm work or by employing outside labour. In their study of farmers who had recently taken industrial jobs in two communities in the west of Ireland, Lucey and Kaldor (1969:168–71) discovered that the most usual response of farmers was to increase the amount of time that their wives spent in farm work, the least common to increase the use of hired labour. Higgins (1983:67) concluded that the farmer's wife was the most important member of the labour force after the farmer, making some contribution on 56 per cent of all Irish part-time farms. The situation in England and Wales is much the same, between half and two-thirds of all part-time farmers being assisted by their wives (or husbands) on the farm. The farm survey estimated that wives helped on a regular basis on nearly half the part-time holdings in the country and occasionally on a further 15 per cent. On the remaining

Table 4.4 Time worked by spouses on part-time farms in 1983/4

Time worked	Estimated number of holdings	Per cent
Full-time	3 681 *c*	7.1
Part-time	21 376 *b*	40.9
Seasonal/occasional	7 980 *b*	15.2
No farm work	12 912 *b*	24.6
No spouse	6 395 *c*	12.2
All holdings	52 344	100.0

(*Source*: 1984 farm survey, raised results)

37 per cent of holdings there was either no spouse or the spouse had done no farm work in the previous twelve months (Table 4.4).

The amount of farm work the farmer does is closely related to the size of the holding, the number of workers employed and the level and importance of farm income to the household. The amount of farm work contributed by the spouse is not significantly affected by these economic considerations but is more sensitive than the farmer's labour input to stage in the family cycle as Table 4.5 shows. Wives appear to make their greatest contribution on the farm in the early stage of family development when they have young children at home. They are somewhat less likely to work regularly on the farm when they have sons and daughters of working age and less likely still when the empty-nest stage is reached or if parents or in-laws live with the family. This pattern probably reflects a combination of factors

Table 4.5 Time worked by spouses on part-time farms and stage in the family cycle

Stage in cycle	Regular	Occasional	No work/no spouse	All holdings
		per cent of holdings		
Early	60.6	17.7	21.7	100.0
Middle	52.7	17.8	29.5	100.0
Empty nest	49.2	16.9	33.9	100.0
Parental generation	42.9	26.5	30.6	100.0
Incomplete	6.0	0.0	94.0	100.0 ***

(*Source*: 1984 farm survey, sample results)

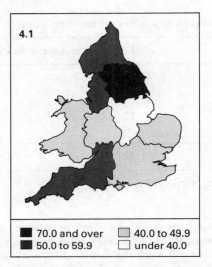

Fig. 4.1 Percentage of spouses doing farm work on a regular basis.

including greater energy among younger women, the need to build up the farm business in the early stage when money is short, and older children or retired parents relieving the farmer's wife of some of her chores at a later stage.

Whether or not wives help on the farm seems to vary a great deal between different parts of the country. Help is more regularly given on farms in northern England and in the west than in the east; it is quite unusual for farmers' wives in Yorkshire and Humberside *not* to be involved in the work of the farm, according to Fig. 4.1. Assistance is least likely to be forthcoming on part-time farms in Wales, the south-east and the East Midlands, either because the farmer is unmarried or because the wife is occupied elsewhere. Figure 3.1 told a similar story, the highest proportion of dual-job spouses being found in Yorkshire, the north-west and south-west and fewest in the south-east and East Anglia.

Wives are less likely than farmers to turn their hands to every kind of task on the farm. More often their labour is channelled in certain directions. On a large farm the farmer's wife may be confined to the farm office, she may lend a hand in emergencies only or she may be given responsibility for specific tasks like lambing, fruit picking or looking after poultry. On smaller part-time farms wives are more likely to tackle any job, if indeed they are required to help at all.

OTHER FAMILY LABOUR ON THE FARM

Although most part-time farms could be described as family-worked farms, the labour contribution of other family members is often quite small. From the farm survey it was estimated that only two adult members of the household had done any farm work in the previous twelve months on over half the part-time holdings; no account was taken of work by children still in full-time education. Since many farmers are assisted by their spouses the contribution from sons and daughters must have been quite small. Only one part-time farm in six recorded more than two family members doing farm work.

Chapter 3 described how numbers of household members who were economically active on or off the farm varied by farm size and region, being greatest on larger farms and in the East Midlands, Yorkshire/Humberside and north-west regions and least on small holdings, in the south-east of England and in Wales. Numbers working on the family farm show the same general tendencies although the association with holding size was only significant at the 10 per cent level. Variations in numbers of family workers by region and stage in the family cycle were sharper. As Fig. 4.2 shows, households with two or more members working on the farm besides the farmer were a feature of northern England, particularly of the Yorkshire/Humberside and north-west regions. In eastern England and in Wales it was more usual to find the farmer alone involved in farm work which confirms what has already been discovered about farm work by wives (Fig. 4.1). Most of the households with two or more members assisting the farmer on the holding were in the middle stage of the family cycle, a stage which occurred more frequently in Yorkshire and the north-west. The prevalence of incomplete families in the south-east and 'empty nests' in East Anglia helps to explain why few members of the family were available for farm work.

Earlier the possibility of labour substitution within the part-time farming family was raised. There was some suggestion in Chapter 3 that wives might be standing in for absent husbands on the smaller part-time farms although this relationship did not extend to the larger holdings. It does not appear to extend to other members of the household either since numbers of household members working on the farm are greater and not less where the farmer is more heavily involved. As Table 4.6 shows, those farmers who work full time on the home farm are the most likely to be assisted by two or more other members of the family, those putting in an occasional appearance or doing no farm work at all, the least likely. Similarly in the Wisconsin study Kada (1980: 56) found that the more hours the farmer worked, the heavier was the farm-labour contribution of younger members of the family.

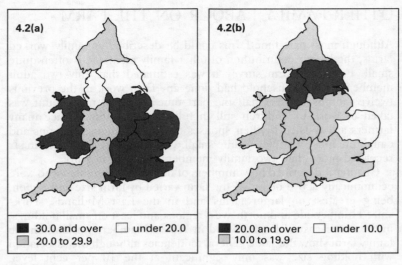

Fig. 4.2 Regional variations in extent to which other household members help on the farm.
  (a) Percentage of farmers without assistance on the farm from other members of the household.
  (b) Percentage of farmers assisted on the farm by two or more household members.

Table 4.6 Time worked by farmers and number of household members assisting on the holding

| Time farmer works on holding | Number of household members assisting farmer on farm | | | |
	none	one	two or more	all holdings
	per cent of holdings			
Full-time	19.5	57.4	23.1	100.0
Part-time	27.7	57.4	14.9	100.0
Occasionally or not at all	73.0	25.0	2.0	100.0
All farmers	29.1	54.8	16.1	100.0 ***
Estimated numbers	15 229 *b*	28 673 *a*	8 442 *b*	52 344

(*Source*: 1984 farm survey, sample results)

EMPLOYMENT OF NON-FAMILY LABOUR

Another possibility is that non-family labour is substituted for farmers, spouses and other members of the farm household who choose to work elsewhere. Roughly one part-time farm in four employs some non-family labour on a regular basis according to the farm survey. This is close to the figure for all agricultural holdings in England and Wales, a surprising result in view of the small size of many part-time farms. Rather more than half the labour employing part-time farms have just one worker and few have more than three. Together they employ just over 25 000 workers as Table 4.7 shows.

Table 4.7 Employment of non-family labour on part-time holdings

Regular employees per holding	Estimated number of holdings	Per cent	Numbers employed
None	38 813 *a*	74.2	–
One	7 250 *b*	13.8	7 250
Two	2 605 *c*	5.0	5 210
Three	2 062 *c*	3.9	6 186
Four or more	1 614 *c*	3.1	more than 6 456
All holdings	52 344	100.0	more than 25 102

(*Source*: 1984 farm survey, raised results)

Employment of non-family labour is closely linked with size of farm, rising from 12 per cent in band 1 to 66 per cent in band 4. Almost all the farms with more than two regular workers are in band 4 as expected. The greatest concentration of large labour forces is to be found in East Anglia. Wales has the most farms without employees but regional differences were not, in this case, statistically significant.

The farm survey produced little evidence of non-family workers being substituted for farmers who had other jobs. Farmers who worked full time on the farm were the most likely to employ outside labour, those working part time the least likely. The only hint of a substitution effect is in the last column of figures in Table 4.8 which suggests that those farmers who did no regular work on their farms were the most likely to be employing three or more workers. Oblique support came from the pilot study which found that farmers who were members of the professional and managerial classes and those running their own businesses were significantly more likely than other part-time farmers to employ workers on the farm while those employed in the manual and service sectors were the least likely to do so.

Table 4.8 Employment of non-family labour by time farmer works on holding

Regular employees per holding	Time worked by farmer on holding		
	full-time	part-time	occasionally/none
	per cent of holdings		
None	56.6	76.5	67.3
One or two	30.6	16.6	17.3
Three or more	12.8	6.9	15.4
All holdings	100.0	100.0	100.0 ***

(*Source*: 1984 farm survey, sample results)

Part-time farmers who cannot handle all the work on the holding themselves but cannot afford to employ workers on a regular basis may make use of alternative sources of labour such as agricultural contractors, seasonal or casual workers. More than half of all part-time farmers, according to the farm survey, make use of one or more of these alternatives in the course of a normal year. A few rely on them to a large extent including some who employ contractors for all the farming operations. Nearly half use contractors or seasonal workers to a small extent, typically for tasks like haymaking, combining and baling, fruit picking and shearing.

Use of alternative sources of labour is heaviest on the largest holdings, those which are already employing the most regular labour and where the family labour input is also the greatest (Table 4.9). There is little evidence here of alternative sources of labour being substituted for members of the farm family who have other jobs. Size of farm would seem to have an overriding influence on labour inputs on the part-time farm. If there is a substitution effect it is masked by the much stronger farm-size effect.

One aspect of labour use not investigated in the present survey was reliance on informal arrangements like mutual aid, that is to say the exchange of unpaid help between neighbours, relatives or friends. In some parts of England and Wales such arrangements are widely used to overcome peaks of labour demand on the smaller farm. McQuin (1978) discovered a high degree of cooperation between occupiers of 'rural retreats' or hobby farms in the Armidale area of New South Wales. Half the sample was involved in the exchange of specialised skills and equipment and 'working bees' on labour-intensive schemes. Cooperation was most widespread in the building of fences but it could also involve assistance with calvings, shearing and

Table 4.9 Use of alternative sources of labour by size of holding

| Size band | Use of seasonal, casual and contractor labour on holding | | | |
	large	small	not at all	total
	per cent of holdings			
1	5.1	39.1	55.8	100.0
2	9.9	58.5	31.6	100.0
3	12.0	53.8	34.2	100.0
4	23.1	47.8	29.1	100.0
All holdings	9.6	45.8	44.6	100.0 ***
Estimated numbers	5 028 *b*	23 993 *a*	23 323 *a*	52 344

(*Source*: 1984 farm survey, raised results)

stock movements and overseeing the property when the owner was away. On the other hand the OECD report noted that part-time farmers were considerably less likely than full-time farmers to cooperate in making fuller use of machinery through 'machinery rings'.

EMPLOYMENT GENERATED BY PART-TIME FARMING

One of the arguments advanced to support part-time farming is that it could help to maintain a stable level of population in rural areas. Its contribution is thought to be particularly important in remote and disadvantaged rural regions where it may enable more people to make a living than could survive by farming alone. Apart from preventing depopulation, part-time farming might have a more positive role to play by helping to bring new jobs to rural areas.

On balance there is little evidence that part-time farming is bringing additional employment to the countryside. The farm surveys produced scant indication of any labour being substituted for absent part-time farmers. In any case as Heatherington (1983) has pointed out, this would be a neutral employment effect since no extra jobs are created. A positive employment effect would be the creation of new jobs in the rural area.

Most of those employed by part-time farming households work on farms. As this chapter has shown, employment of non-family labour on the farm is closely linked with the size of the holding. It bears little relation to the farmer's involvement in other activities. Whilst about one part-time farm family in four employed labour on the holding, about one in nine had paid help in the house. Here again farm size appeared to be the crucial influence. Employment of non-family labour in the farmhouse rose from 7 per cent of households in bands 1 and 2 to 19 per cent in band 4. It bore no relation to stage in the family cycle or to the spouse's having another paid job. Ability to pay rather than the amount of work the farmer's wife has to do would seem to be the main consideration in this case.

Fewer than one part-time farming household in ten employed labour in any non-farm occupation. Here it was the nature of the other occupation and its contribution to total household income rather than farm size that played a decisive role. The jobs were not necessarily available in the rural area, however. Some of the largest employers had businesses in London and commuted to their farms in the Home Counties or even beyond. Only 55 of the 700 part-time farming families in the sample employed non-family workers in other businesses based on the holding. On balance, then, the potential of part-time farming for creating new jobs in the countryside does not appear to be very great. Most rural employment is associated with the largest part-time farms and most of the jobs are still in agriculture where the scope for growth is not likely to be large. Employment in other activities associated with part-time farming is mostly confined to farmers and members of their families. The next chapter considers the nature of these other occupations.

The nature of other occupations

TRENDS IN OTHER ACTIVITIES

One of the most striking features of part-time farming is the diversity of other activities which farmers and members of their families manage to combine with running a farm. Among the occupations discovered in the farm surveys were Member of Parliament, chairman of a multi-national corporation, racing-car driver, undertaker, artist, engine driver, bomb-disposal expert and a nun who made grandfather clocks. People in every conceivable occupation, it seems, may also farm. There is nevertheless some degree of regularity with some types of employment cropping up more frequently than others. The pattern varies over time and space but when information from a number of studies is brought together, certain broad trends begin to emerge.

In some regions of Britain, as in Europe and North America, there has been a long tradition of farming as a main occupation being associated with some particular second activity. Farming, forestry and fishing and related processing industries, mining and quarrying, have in the past provided seasonal work for many part-time farmers. A general trend since the Second World War has been away from such manual, seasonal or casual, rural-based second jobs towards full-time, off-farm, urban-based employment not necessarily linked to agriculture. Consequently the other activities are tending to take over from farming as the main source of income and employment in part-time farming households. While declining farm incomes and rising aspirations have impelled many farm families along this road, improved transport and communications, decentralisation of industry and sustained economic growth since the early 1950s have made a far wider range of occupations available to farmers and members of their families.

TYPES OF OCCUPATION

The classification of farmers' and spouses' other activities which was developed for the 1983 EC structure survey emphasises the traditional rural occupations but does not do justice to what is happening on farms in England and Wales today. As Table 5.1 shows, nearly two-thirds of other jobs come into the undifferentiated category of 'other paid work off the holding' while very small numbers are involved in forestry and fishing, craft industry and other work on the holding. The only other categories of any significance are accommodation and tourism on the holding, for spouses, and farm work elsewhere, for farmers. Compared with the Community as a whole the UK has easily the largest proportion of occupiers engaged in farm-based tourism and above average numbers doing farm work elsewhere with relatively fewer involved in craft industry at home or in other gainful activities off the holding (Robson 1987).

In the 1984 farm survey a different classification was used. Activities taking place off the holding were divided into *work on other farms*

Table 5.1 The nature of farmers' and spouses' other paid work on farms in England and Wales, 1983

Type of work	Farmers	Spouses
	per cent of other jobs	
Work on the holding		
Accommodation or catering for tourists or holidaymakers	6.7	21.1
Craft work such as pottery, ironwork etc.	1.7	1.9
Other paid work on the holding	7.4	7.0
Work off the holding		
Farm work for someone else	19.7	5.6
Forestry or fishing	2.3	0.3
Other paid work off the holding	62.2	64.1
All paid work	100.0	100.0

(*Source*: provisional results of 1983 LII)

and *off-farm work*. The latter, easily the largest group, was sub-divided into business, professional, service and manual occupations.

Off-farm work

Business occupations, that is to say being an owner, partner, director or manager of a business, covered a wide spectrum. At one extreme were those involved in 'big business' as bankers, stockbrokers, insurance brokers, underwriters, directors of multinationals and the like, at the other those running small family businesses or one-man firms such as small shops, garages and repair firms. In between came firms operating at less than national level but employing non-family labour; small manufacturing, wholesale and retail businesses, engin-eering and building firms were typical of this group.

The criterion for a *professional* occupation was an entry requirement of a degree or equivalent qualification involving full-time training for at least three years. The pilot and 1984 farm surveys produced a few members of 'higher' professions such as doctors and lawyers who would have undergone a longer training period but most professionals had occupations like teacher, lecturer, nurse, physiotherapist, social worker, librarian, accountant and surveyor.

In the *service* category came clerical, secretarial, technical, sales, administrative and personal service occupations for which the entry requirement would normally be less than a university degree. Jobs which cropped up frequently included typist, computer operator, wages clerk, shop assistant, sales representative, laboratory tech-nician, hairdresser, caterer, florist and teacher's aide. Often these jobs are performed by women and Deseran (1984) has coined the term 'pink-collar jobs'.

Manual occupations can be subdivided into supervisory (for example foreman), skilled manual (mechanic, printer, joiner), semi-skilled and unskilled (county council roadman, factory worker, forklift truck driver, domestic worker, cleaner).

Work on other farms

The second major category was work on other farms by which was meant holdings which were completely separate businesses from those which were drawn in the sample. This did not include work on other holdings which were part of the same business structure nor the exchange of mutual aid between farms.

Work on other farms was divided into agricultural contracting, wage work and management. Typical tasks undertaken by *agricultural contractors* in the sample were ploughing, spraying, silage making, combining, baling, manure spreading, hedge cutting and ditching. A number of farm-family members were *wage workers* on other farms, some as regular or casual employees and others on a self-employed basis providing special services such as relief milking, contract shepherding, shearing, fencing or pruning. An interesting example was a service of 'helping hands' for smallholders. In the *management* category were those running quite separate farm businesses on their own account, those who were partners or directors in other farm businesses and those earning a management fee or salary for professional advice. Examples here included a farmer managing his late father's farm many miles away for his mother and a young farmer who worked on his father-in-law's farm but also ran a broiler unit on his own account.

Farm-based enterprises

Work taking place on the holding was divided into *farm-based enterprises* and *home businesses*. While the distinction was not always clear, a farm base was felt to be essential for the first but not for the second. Farm-based enterprises were subdivided into providing accommodation, catering for sporting and recreational interests and adding value to farm products.

Activities *providing accommodation* and catering for tourists and holidaymakers on the holding included farmhouse bed-and-breakfast enterprises, farm hotels, restaurants and pubs and the letting of self-catering accommodation in the form of caravan and camping sites, cottages, flats, chalets and caravans on the farm. More unusual activities included wardening a youth hostel, running a homoeopathic hydro and a religious centre based on the Benedictine order which offered residential courses and retreats.

Among the *sporting and recreational* enterprises were the breeding, breaking in, training and racing of horses, riding stables, pony-trekking centres and do-it-yourself livery stables where horse owners pay a rent for stabling but are personally responsible for feeding, grooming, cleaning out and exercising their animals. Breeding and boarding dogs, training greyhounds, breeding endangered species, letting shooting and fishing rights and opening facilities (for instance gardens, a woodland trail, a steam-engine collection) to the public were also included under this heading.

Adding value to farm products similarly covered a wide range of activities. Examples encountered in the farm survey included grain drying, cold storage of meat and fruit for other farms, the manufacture of cream, butter, yoghurt and cheese, curing bacon, making cider, bottling spring water and processing straw into logs. A great variety of produce is sold through farm shops, plant nurseries and garden centres, retail rounds, mobile shops and mail-order businesses including milk, eggs, meat, fish, game, potatoes, vegetables, flowers, herbs, plants, seeds, floral decorations, turf, logs, wood for carving, thatching spars and stakes.

Home businesses

The farm survey revealed a great variety of other small businesses being run from farm addresses and it was difficult to find any common thread. Types which appeared frequently included building, haulage, engineering and plant-hire firms. Occupations traditionally associated with part-time farming like agricultural merchant and cattle dealer

Table 5.2 Activities on part-time farms in England and Wales

Type of activity	Estimated numbers	Per cent of part-time holdings	Per cent of all main holdings
Off-farm work			
Business	6 781 *b*		
Profession	7 086 *b*		
Service	11 109 *b*		
Manual	9 420 *b*		
All off-farm work	34 396 *a*	65.7	20.2
Work on other farms			
Management	2 582 *c*		
Contracting	4 929 *c*		
Wage work	4 957 *c*		
All work on other farms	12 468 *b*	23.8	7.3
Farm-based enterprises			
Providing accommodation	4 489 *c*		
Sporting and recreation	3 125 *c*		
Adding value to products	3 823 *c*		
All farm-based enterprises	11 437 *b*	21.8	6.7
Home businesses			
Home workshop	7 090		
Home agency	4 995 *c*		
All home businesses	12 085 *b*	23.1	7.1

(*Source*: 1984 farm survey, raised results)

were joined by newer ones like agricultural training officer. Activities with a modern flavour included property development, car breaking, industrial roofing, recycling paper and designing kitchen units.

A distinction might be made between those home businesses requiring a home workshop or office and those which involve going out to meet clients although some activities like building and transport combine elements of both. In the *home workshop* category are small-scale engineering, repair and manufacturing businesses; for example, firms designing and building farm trailers. Handcrafts encountered in the sample included pottery, wood carving, making harness and saddlery, painting, knitting and embroidery and making and restoring clocks. Under the *home agency* heading were freelance architects, surveyors, secretaries and teachers, local agents and organisers for such bodies as the Agricultural Training Board and the Country Landowners' Association. The growing band of private agricultural consultants represented in the sample included specialists in livestock, wool, machinery, fertilisers, agricultural marketing and landscape gardening.

Table 5.2 gives the sample-based estimates of numbers of agricultural holdings in England and Wales involved in each type of activity. A holding can be involved in more than one activity so the total exceeds the number of part-time farms. The table confirms the importance of non-farm off-farm work. Nearly two-thirds of all part-time holdings in the country have at least one household member with an off-farm job and this is equivalent to one-fifth of all main agricultural holdings in England and Wales. Work on other farms, farm-based enterprises and home businesses account for some 11 000 to 12 000 holdings each, between a quarter and a fifth of all part-time farms or about 7 per cent of all holdings.

REGIONAL VARIATIONS

In their survey of part-time farming in the 1950s Ashton and Cracknell (1961) noticed some marked regional characteristics in the types of non-farm occupations followed by farmers. In the eastern region there was a concentration of occupiers who were also farm workers and agricultural contractors. Forestry workers were found particularly in northern England and Wales, quarrymen and miners mainly in Wales and boarding-house proprietors in the south-west. Studies in the Home Counties have revealed concentrations of part-time farmers who were also members of professions or executives in city businesses (Harrison 1965:332; Gasson 1966:21–2).

Table 5.3 Types of activity by region

Region	Off-farm work	Work on other farms	Farm-based enterprises	Home businesses
	per cent of part-time farms involved			
North	55.4	19.9	30.2	29.3
Yorks/Humber	76.0	36.0	12.6	23.3
E. Midland	65.6	29.0	7.6	33.6
East Anglia	55.0	24.7	11.1	17.3
South-east	76.3	24.0	20.8	24.2
South-west	59.6	27.7	36.3	21.7
W. Midland	70.3	22.2	19.7	6.6
North-west	54.5	13.9	17.1	33.3
Wales	67.1	14.1	21.9	25.3
All regions	65.7	23.8	21.8	23.1
	**	ns	***	**

(*Source*: 1984 farm survey, raised results)

The present survey, too, revealed some significant differences in the regional distribution of other activities (Table 5.3). Off-farm work, the most important type of activity in every region, was especially prominent in the south-east of England and the Yorkshire/Humberside region where more than three out of every four part-time farms was involved. Business occupations appeared to be most widespread in the east and south and also in north-west England, professions being more characteristic of the western parts of England. Farming combined with manual work seemed to be most common in the north-eastern half of the country and employment in service industries, of Wales.

Regional differences in the nature of work done on other farms were not significant although the Yorkshire/Humberside region stood out as having the most farm-family members involved in agricultural contracting and wage work on other farms. Northern England, the Midlands and the south-west were also prominent in these activities while East Anglia had the most part-time farmers who were also engaged in managing other farms.

Farm-based enterprises were more important in the south-west and north of England than elsewhere. Nearly one part-time farm in five in these regions was providing accommodation or catering for tourists in some form. Wales came next in importance. Sporting and recreational enterprises were well represented in these three regions and also in the south-east. More densely populated regions may offer greater scope for direct sales of farm produce to the public. Activities like producer retailing of milk appeared to be very popular in the north-west of England where 17 per cent of all part-time farms were involved in enterprises adding value to farm products.

Home businesses were most common in the East Midlands and north-west regions, two parts of the country with a long-established industrial base. 'Home-workshop' activities like building, manufacture and repair work were found on more than a fifth of all part-time farms in the north and north-west of England, Yorkshire and the East Midlands while 'home agencies' were most widespread in the south-west, north-west and Wales.

Few of the associations between the finer occupational categories and region were found to be statistically significant. The standard region may not be the most appropriate unit to capture geographical variations. A region like Yorkshire and Humberside, for example, includes areas as diverse as the North York moors, the warplands of Humberside and industrial West Yorkshire. A number of other geographical breakdowns was tested. The pilot study found that farm tourism was much more significant in the peripheral regions while enterprises using land for non-agricultural purposes such as horse paddocks, livery stables, riding schools and boarding kennels dominated in the central belt of England running from London through the Midlands to the conurbations of the north-west. Part-time farmers running off-farm businesses were found to be concentrated close to urban areas while the service occupations were over-represented in the most rural areas. Manual occupations seemed to fall in between whilst professions were more or less evenly spread across all locations.

An attempt was made to measure the degree of urban influence on the holdings drawn for the main survey. The criterion chosen was Cloke's Index of Rurality (Cloke 1977) which has proved a useful tool for comparing rural areas. As Cloke has been careful to point out, the Index is intended to measure *rural* influence; it cannot be assumed that this is necessarily the opposite of urban. Cloke measured a total of sixteen variables for each rural district in England and Wales using population census data and maps. The variables were chosen to indicate rurality and included population density and age structure, migration and commuting to work, occupational structure and distance from large urban centres. Using principal components analysis Cloke calculated an index of rurality for each district in 1961 and 1971.

Each holding in the main sample was allocated to one of the rural districts on Cloke's list and scored with his 1971 index. This was necessarily a rough-and-ready procedure involving a number of assumptions. To avoid giving any spurious impression of accuracy the sample was divided into quartiles from 'most rural' to 'least rural'. Off-farm jobs were found to be significantly associated with the less rural end of the spectrum while farm-based enterprises were concentrated in the most rural areas. No significant association could be detected between the degree of rurality and the incidence of work on other farms or home businesses. It would not have been surprising to find home businesses, like off-farm work, concentrated in the least rural areas. An earlier study of farming in the urban fringe commented on 'the growth of shanty-type non-agricultural enterprises such as scrapyards, small haulage depots, paint-spraying workshops and so on' (Ministry of Agriculture, Fisheries and Food 1973:12).

THE INFLUENCE OF FARM SIZE

None of the geographical breakdowns tested proved to have a very strong association with the nature of other occupations. This seems to imply *either* that the correct variables have not been specified *or* that geographical influence over the distribution of other occupations in part-time farming families is not very strong. Farm size appeared to be much more closely related to the nature of other occupations than any of the geographical variables. Off-farm work and home businesses, especially significant for farms in the smallest size band, decline in importance as farm size increases while the more rural and farm-based activities come to assume greater prominence. According to the survey holdings in band 4 (500 smd and above) were twice as likely as those in band 1 (under 100 smd) to have household members involved in work on other farms or farm-based enterprises.

Table 5.4 Types of activity by size of holding

Size band	Off-farm work	Work on other farms	Farm-based enterprise	Home business
	per cent of part-time farms involved			
1	72.9	15.8	16.6	25.7
2	58.4	30.9	22.2	23.8
3	60.3	31.5	25.7	20.2
4	53.7	37.2	36.7	15.4
All holdings	65.7	23.8	21.8	23.1
	***	***	***	***

(*Source*: 1984 farm survey, raised results)

Table 5.5 Nature of farmers' off-farm occupations by size of holding

Size band	Business	Profession	Service	Manual	All off-farm jobs
	per cent of farmers' off-farm jobs				
1	26.6	21.4	19.4	32.6	100.0
2	26.3	17.3	17.8	38.6	100.0
3	36.4	11.7	13.6	38.3	100.0
4	51.3	13.3	17.7	17.7	100.0
All holdings	29.7	19.2	18.5	32.6	100.0 ***

(*Source*: 1984 farm survey, raised results)

Within each of the broad occupational categories, too, there appears to be a grading of activities according to farm size. In the category of off-farm work, for instance, running a second business is especially associated with the larger farms; Table 5.5 shows that over half of all farmers' off-farm jobs in band 4 come under the 'business' heading, roughly double the proportion in bands 1 and 2. Manual and service occupations are more characteristic of smaller farms. The pilot study did not find any part-time farmers in the top size band who were manual or service workers. Farmers who are members of professions tend to be associated with the smallest farms, on the evidence of the main survey, although the pilot found a bimodal distribution with farmer-professionals clustered on the smallest and the largest holdings. For farmers' wives, by contrast, the importance of professional employment increases steadily with farm size. In the smallest size band fewer than a quarter of all spouses' off-farm jobs came into the professional category, in the top size band nearly half.

Both the main and the pilot studies found that more spouses than farmers held relevant qualifications for their off-farm occupations such as a degree, a teaching diploma or an apprenticeship. The link between farm size and possession of a qualification works in the opposite direction for farmers and for spouses although, as Table 5.6 shows, the association is not significant for spouses. The larger the farm, the more likely it is that the farmer's wife will be qualified for her off-farm job and the less likely that the farmer will be qualified for his. This ties up with the prevalence of professional employment for farmers on very small holdings and for spouses on larger farms. It is consistent with the suggestion in Chapter 3 that for some women

Table 5.6 Qualifications for farmers' and spouses' off-farm jobs by size of holding

Size band	Farmers	Spouses
	per cent with relevant qualifications	
1	45.6	44.7
2	34.7	44.5
3	35.1	49.8
4	24.9	53.1
All holdings	41.4	46.2
	***	ns

(*Source*: 1984 farm survey, raised results)

on larger farms, having a job outside the farm may be important for motives of career development and personal fulfilment as well as for financial reasons.

Among farm-related activities the influence of farm size is most noticeable. Farm management, agricultural contracting, providing accommodation and adding value to farm products all occur most frequently on the largest part-time farms and least often on the smallest. According to the farm survey agricultural contracting involved under 5 per cent of holdings in band 1 but nearly 18 per cent of those in band 4. Under 5 per cent of all part-time farms in band 1 but over 20 per cent in band 4 ran tourist enterprises of some kind. Activities like these can perhaps be introduced more easily on larger farms where they may make use of available resources like vacant farm buildings, redundant cottages, spare machinery capacity or an unused corner of the farm. Those farmers with larger enterprises may also be in a better position to raise capital for building conversions and to launch other businesses.

OCCUPATION AND POSITION IN THE HOUSEHOLD

The way other occupations are allocated within the family reflects the prevailing norms of society. Within each occupational category those jobs which are higher in status and authority tend to be held by farmers. For instance 71 per cent of farmers working on other farms were either farm managers or agricultural contractors and only 29 per cent were employees whereas 68 per cent of spouses and 73 per cent of other household members were hired farm workers. Farmers in the sample held 27 of the 31 positions in 'big business' while other members of farm households were more often found in middle-sized businesses and small family firms. Farmers claimed 10 of the 12 'higher' professional posts like doctor and vet while wives and daughters accounted for 87 of the 121 'lower' posts such as teacher and social worker. In the manual category farmers held 12 of the 15 supervisory posts, spouses 15 of the 20 unskilled jobs.

Activities are also divided in a predictable way by sex. In the off-farm category farmers tend towards business and manual occupations whilst the majority of spouses have professional and service jobs. (As already shown, more spouses than farmers hold qualifications for off-farm work.) Teaching, nursing and secretarial work head the list of other jobs for farmers' wives. Similarly in the United States, over half the farmers' wives with off-farm employment are in clerical and professional jobs (Jones and Rosenfeld 1981:42–3). Provision of tourist accommodation is usually a woman's province whilst sporting and recreational enterprises and adding value to farm products involve more farmers than wives. More than half the working sons of farmers are in manual occupations and more than two-thirds of the daughters work in the service sector (Table 5.7).

Table 5.7 Off-farm occupation and position in household

Type of work	Farmer	Spouse	Other	All household members
	per cent of off-farm jobs			
Business	29.5	14.6	9.5	19.8
Profession	19.2	30.5	9.1	20.7
Service	18.4	39.6	47.2	32.4
Manual	32.9	15.3	34.2	27.1
All off-farm jobs	100.0	100.0	100.0	100.0 ***

(*Source*: 1984 farm survey, sample results)

EMPLOYMENT STATUS

The previous section suggested that work roles on and off the farm tend to mirror authority patterns within the family. One manifestation of this is that the majority of British part-time farmers are self-employed in their second job while wives and children are usually employees. The pilot study found that 65 per cent of part-time farmers were running second businesses on their own account and the main survey, using a more reliable sample, gave an estimate of 70 per cent while Harrison (1975:14) calculated that as many as 77 per cent of part-time farmers in England gained their additional income as proprietors of second businesses. About 40 per cent of business owners, according to the 1984 farm survey, employ others while the rest are self-employed without hired non-family labour.

Farmers who were wage or salaried employees accounted for only 30 per cent of all dual-job farmers but 55 per cent of those with off-farm occupations. In all other categories most farmers worked on their own account. Those involved in farm-based enterprises were the most likely to employ others and the least likely to be employed themselves (Table 5.8). Farmer employers were found to be concentrated on the eastern side of England from Yorkshire to the south-east and were also numerous in the north-west region. There was a striking contrast here between England and Wales for more than half the Welsh part-time farmers were employed by others in contrast to no more than a third in any of the English regions. The predominance of service occupations for Welsh part-time farmers may help to account for this.

Table 5.8 Employment status of farmers and type of occupation

Type of work	Employer	Self-employed, no workers	Employee	All dual-job farmers
	per cent of farmers' other jobs			
Off-farm work	24.8	20.6	54.6	100.0
Work on other farms	20.2	62.1	17.7	100.0
Home business	30.7	57.5	11.8	100.0
Farm-based enterprise	46.7	49.8	3.5	100.0
All activities	28.2	41.6	30.2	100.0 ***

(*Source*: 1984 farm survey, raised results)

Any occupation dominated by business proprietors is likely to be weighted towards the older age groups. The 1983 LII revealed a tendency for those farmers who had other occupations on the holding, which were almost by definition their own businesses, to be older than those working off the holding. As Table 5.9 shows over 10 per cent of the part-time farmers involved in tourism, crafts and other work on the holding were aged 65 or older as against fewer than 7

Table 5.9 Type of activity and farmers' age

Type of activity	Per cent of farmers who were:	
	under 35	65 and over
Farm tourism	4.6	12.7
Craft work on the holding	3.7	12.1
Other work on the holding	9.2	11.4
Farm work elsewhere	19.7	6.3
Forestry or fishing	14.1	2.9
Other work off the holding	9.6	5.9
All activities	10.7	6.8

(*Source*: provisional results of 1983 LII)

per cent who went to work elsewhere. Work on other farms, forestry and fishing were particularly associated with younger men who would presumably have sufficient energy to cope with another outdoor, manual job on top of running a farm.

Being self-employed in the second job gives the farmer a degree of flexibility in the way he allocates his time, an advantage not shared by employees. If necessary he can leave the other job to attend to essential tasks on the farm although in practice such freedom may be enjoyed by proprietors of one-man firms rather than by directors and managers of large companies. Kada (1980:107, 119) cited self employment as one of the main adjustments which part-time farmers in the United States and Japan made to dual-job holding. In Britain it is not unusual for someone taking over a farm to continue with the previous non-farm occupation but to change from being an employee to self-employed status; for example from dairy cowman to self-employed relief milker. Besides this, Table 5.6 suggested that only a minority of farmers hold the kinds of qualification which would be necessary for entry to the better paid high-status jobs in a modern industrial society. This would make running a second business seem more attractive by comparison.

Many of the second businesses which farmers run make use of farm resources such as land, buildings or machinery and farm land might be used as security to raise capital for the second business. This could help to account for the highly significant association between size of farm and the farmer's employment status in his second job. According to Table 5.10 the proportion of farmers who were employees dropped from 36 per cent in band 1 to 14 per cent in band 4 while the proportion who were self-employed rose. The likelihood

Table 5.10 Employment status of farmers and size of holding

Size band	Employer	Self-employed, no workers	Employee	All dual-job farmers
		per cent of farmers		
1	24.1	40.0	35.9	100.0
2	27.1	45.3	27.6	100.0
3	32.3	43.5	24.2	100.0
4	43.1	43.0	13.9	100.0
All holdings	28.2	41.6	30.2	100.0 ***

(*Source*: 1984 farm survey, raised results)

that the farmer would employ others in his second business was still more closely linked with farm size, rising from 24 per cent in band 1 to 43 per cent in band 4. The 1975 structure survey found that the proportion of occupiers who were self-employed in a second job was about half on holdings below 275 smd but three-quarters on holdings of 275 smd and over (Ministry of Agriculture, Fisheries and Food 1976).

The link between farm size and self-employment may help to explain why such a high proportion of British farmers are proprietors of second businesses. The 1975 structure survey established that the proportion of farmers working outside agriculture who were self-employed was 45 per cent in the UK but only 26 per cent in the Community as a whole (Commission 1980). If the proportion of British part-time farmers who run other businesses is exceptionally high it may only be an extreme example of a common trend. Alden and Spooner (1981:98) reported that self-employment in the second job was a marked feature of multiple job holding in all countries of the Community. A study in eastern Ontario found that over 70 per cent of local non-farm jobs held by part-time farmers were on a self-employed or franchise basis although jobs performed beyond the local area were always of employee status (Bunce 1976:252). In Ireland 32 per cent of part-time farmers but only 10 per cent of the non-agricultural workforce were self-employed in 1978. Again there was a strong link between farm size, a prosperous farming area and self-employment in the second job (Higgins 1983:16–19).

The discovery that most British part-time farmers are proprietors of second businesses runs counter to the 'proletarianisation' thesis which has been advanced by some rural sociologists. The Marxian theory of historical change postulates that proletarianisation – the separation of persons from their means of production and subsistence – follows in the wake of capitalist development. In the past most of those separated from the means of agricultural production left farming altogether to seek employment in the city. Nowadays, so it is suggested, these marginalised farming families who take up paid employment will be increasingly likely to remain living on their farms as part-time farmers (Goss, Rodefeld and Buttel 1979:45–7). Buttel (1982:293) goes so far as to restrict his definition of part-time farming to those who derive off-farm income through wage labour excluding business profits, rent, interest, royalties and social security as constituting off-farm wage income. He does warn, however, that the growth of part-time farming should not be viewed as proletarianisation in the traditional sense. From the vantage point of the non-farm industrial and commercial sectors where most part-time farmers are employed the development could equally represent a process of embourgeoisement. Part-time farmer-employees are likely to identify with the interests of capital and will be unlikely to align with the non-farm working class in opposition to the interests of their employers.

TIME SPENT IN OTHER ACTIVITIES

At the beginning of this chapter it was suggested that seasonal or temporary employment in the second job, often manual- and rural-based, is giving way to regular full-time employment in urban manufacturing or service industries. More recently there have been signs that the pendulum is swinging away from full-time employment towards part-time self-employed activities which can be performed at home or, at any rate, do not involve long-distance commuting. Signs of a trend towards 'post-industrial' patterns of work are only now beginning to appear in part-time farming. Most of the available survey evidence confirms a general tendency for farmers to work full-time in the other job which they regard as their main occupation. Ashton and Cracknell (1961:484) for instance, estimated that some 41 000 non-farm occupations of part-time farmers were full-time and only 14 500 part-time. In Harrison's national survey 55 per cent of part-time farmers worked at what they claimed were full-time occupations outside the farm (Harrison 1975:13). On small-scale beef and sheep farms in Northern Ireland off-farm work was generally undertaken on a full-time basis and there was little evidence of small-scale farmers having part-time, seasonal or casual off-farm employment (Moss 1980:21). Two-thirds of the part-time farmers in the Republic of Ireland who were wage earners worked full-time in the other job (Higgins 1983:27).

The farm survey found more farmers working full time than part time in their other occupations. Full-time working was the norm for off-farm occupations, part-time work more usual for farm-based enterprises and home businesses and seasonal or casual working for those whose second job took them to other farms (Table 5.11).

Table 5.11 Time farmers spend in other occupations by type of work

Type of work	Full-time	Part-time	Seasonal /casual	All farmers
	per cent of farmers' other jobs			
Off-farm work	67.1	27.4	5.5	100.0
Home business	45.2	49.6	5.2	100.0
Farm-based enterprise	20.1	50.2	29.7	100.0
Work on other farms	17.3	31.7	51.0	100.0
All activities	45.2	36.3	18.5	100.0 ***

(*Source*: 1984 farm survey, raised results)

Table 5.12 illustrates how full-time working in the second job declines as farm size increases. Over half the part-time farmers in band 1 but only one-fifth in band 4 have other full-time jobs. Although seasonal and casual working becomes more common on larger farms, part time working still predominates implying that while the farm side is significant the other job is not necessarily

Table 5.12 Time farmers spend in other occupations by size of holding

Size band	Full-time	Part-time	Seasonal/casual	All farmers
	per cent of farmers' other jobs			
1	56.3	34.0	9.7	100.0
2	38.2	43.2	18.6	100.0
3	28.8	31.6	39.6	100.0
4	20.1	41.9	38.0	100.0
All holdings	45.2	36.3	18.5	100.0 ***

(*Source*: 1984 farm survey, raised results)

unimportant. Some of the largest non-farm business are run by those who have the largest farms.

IMPORTANCE OF THE OTHER OCCUPATION

As Harrison has pointed out,

> There is a tendency, no doubt natural, among agricultural economists and others dealing directly and mainly with farmers, to assume that farming will tend to rank higher in order of priority than other sources of earned income. It is by no means certain that this will always, or even generally, be the case (Harrison 1975:14).

This chapter has referred to the farmer's other job as the *second* occupation but on balance it is likely to be the first one. As already shown more part-time farmers work full time than part time in the other job. Three-quarters of the Irish part-time farmers considered that the off-farm job was their principal occupation (Higgins 1983:16) while farming was the subsidiary occupation for a great majority of part-time farmers in Scotland (Scola 1961; Wagstaff 1970). The 1983 LII ascertained that the other job was the major activity for 58 per cent of dual-job farmers and 59 per cent of spouses in England and Wales. The larger the holding, the more likely it was that farming would come first, an association which was stronger for farmers than for spouses.

Off-farm work is usually the farmer's main occupation; 70 per cent of farmers' off-farm jobs were described as the main occupation in the 1983 LII. Farm tourism is most likely to be a subsidiary activity, only 29 per cent of respondents in the 1983 LII recording a farm tourist enterprise as their main activity. The 1983 LII also showed that farmers who regarded the other job as their main activity were rather more likely than those with another subsidiary activity to be aged between 35 and 55, less likely to be over 55. This could be because older part-time farmers try to cut down on their outside activities. Another possibility is that a new generation of part-time farmers is entering the industry and that these newcomers are more inclined to treat the other job as the main one.

OCCUPATIONS LINKED TO AGRICULTURE

Following the broad trends outlined at the beginning of this chapter, employment of farmers and members of their families has tended to move from primary to secondary and tertiary industries and from rural to urban locations. This can be seen against the background of the changing structure of employment with fewer jobs available in such industries as agriculture, forestry and fishing, mining and manufacturing and more in the service sector.

One consequence has been a decline in the proportion of farmers' other jobs which are linked in some way to agriculture. Comparing the other occupations of Buckinghamshire part-time farmers in 1963 with those recorded in 1936, Harrison (1966:15) noted a decline in the proportion of merchants and dealers who operated mainly on a local basis with the use of land forming an essential part of their trading activities. Between 1941 and 1965 the proportion of farmers' other activities which were related to farming in the Kent and East Sussex parishes had fallen from 54 per cent to 31 per cent (Gasson 1966:23–4). Sometimes the existence of a small or part-time holding reflects a link between farming and another occupation which has become attenuated with the passage of time; accommodation land for the carrier's horse and a glebe for the parish priest have lost their relevance in the late twentieth century. The divorce of the other activity from farming may also signal a trend in part-time farming from economic necessity to amenity.

From the farm survey it was estimated that 57 per cent of all other occupations of part-time farmers were linked in some way to agriculture, slightly lower than the 61 per cent calculated by Harrison for 1969 (Harrison 1975:15–16). Deciding what is and is not 'linked to agriculture' is a subjetive exercise. In the survey the following types of linkage were recognised:

Type of link	*Example*
Using land or space	caravan site, riding stables
Using part of farmhouse	farmhouse bed-and-breakfast
Using farm buildings	letting farm cottages
Using farm produce	farm shop, making farmhouse cheese
Using farm equipment	agricultural contracting, grass cutting
Providing farm inputs	farm consultant, cattle dealer
Similar type of work	gardener, groundsman
Using farm contacts	selling farm insurance, organising an agricultural training group.

Farm-based enterprises and work on other farms were by definition linked to agriculture. About half the home businesses and a quarter of farmers' off-farm jobs were also found to be linked to agriculture, usually because they provided inputs or services to other farms. Examples included the manufacture of farm trailers, a private agricultural consultant based at home and a technician employed in a Ministry of Agriculture laboratory.

The link between farming and the other activity tends to be stronger for farmers (57 per cent of other jobs linked) than for spouses (41 per cent). The pilot study showed a similar pattern with 54 per cent of farmers' and 40 per cent of spouses' other jobs farm-linked. The more rural the area, the more likely was the farmer's other occupation to be linked to agriculture. This holds true for both farmers and spouses as Table 5.13 shows. In the top farm size band more than 80 per cent of farmers' other jobs were related to farming. Once again this seems to underline the fact that it is the operators of the larger farms who are in a better position to develop other enterprises on the holding which require land, buildings or space and to make use of spare machinery capacity, technical knowledge and contacts in order to provide services to other farmers. Families on the smaller holdings are less likely to be involved in farm-related activities either because they lack the necessary resources and contacts or because their comparative advantage lies elsewhere.

Table 5.13 Farmers' and spouses' other occupations linked to agriculture by size of holding

Size band	Farmers	Spouses
	per cent of other jobs linked to agriculture	
1	47.3	34.7
2	65.5	42.0
3	65.3	45.3
4	81.1	54.9
All holdings	57.1	41.0

(*Source*: 1984 farm survey, raised results)

AN OVERVIEW OF OTHER ACTIVITIES

This chapter has shown how the other activities which farmers and their families combine with farming are dominated by non-farm off-farm work. Other activities taking place on the holding and farm work elsewhere are less important. Taking the part-time farming population as a whole the other activity may well take precedence over farming as indicated by the amount of time devoted to each and what the person concerned regards as the main occupation. Many farmers run other businesses which implies competition for funds, management expertise and the proprietor's immediate presence. Clashes over capital allocation and production decisions would seem to be inevitable and it is by no means certain that they would be decided in favour of farming as Harrison (1975:14) has pointed out.

More detailed analysis has revealed a number of cross currents beneath the surface. For one thing, the better paid and more prestigious occupations such as running a business or managing another farm, tend to be associated with larger holdings and with farmers. Occupations which are likely to be less well paid and lower in status, like manual work and routine white-collar jobs, are linked with the smaller holdings and with farmers' wives and children.

Two contrasting types of part-time farming seem to be emerging. On the one hand there are part-time farming households in which the farmer and possibly other household members works full-time in another job for which he is qualified. The occupation will most probably be an off-farm job, the farmer an employee and the work unrelated to agriculture. This constellation of characteristics is typical of holdings in band 1, which is the largest group numerically. It is well represented in the south-east of England, the north-west and the Yorkshire/Humberside region. The other dominant group consists of households where the farmer works part time or occasionally in some other job which is farm-based or farm-related and which he regards as a subsidiary activity. The farmer will most likely be self-employed in this activity and he may employ others although he will probably not have acquired any paper qualifications for it. These 'dual business farmers' as Nalson (1968) termed them are more characteristic of larger farms and they are well represented in East Anglia and the north of England.

The following chapters will build on this idea of contrasting types of part-time farming family. First Chapter 6 explores the contrast in terms of the main source of income.

Chapter

6

Incomes of part-time farming families

TRENDS IN FARM HOUSEHOLD INCOMES

The previous chapter showed how other activities are tending to take precedence over farming for the part-time farming population as a whole. It follows that the other activities are tending to provide a growing share of family income. This chapter is concerned with the relative importance of farming and other sources of earned income for part-time farming families in England and Wales, with an assessment of actual levels of income.

Available evidence suggests that other sources of income are becoming increasingly important for farming families in the world's highly industrialised countries. The share of US farm-family income originating from non-farm sources, for instance, was 26 per cent in 1945, 40 per cent in 1960 and over 60 per cent by the mid-1980s (Carlin and Ghelfi 1979; Ahearn, Johnson and Strickland 1985). Off-farm income per head of the Canadian farm population rose from 12 per cent of total income in 1940 to 59 per cent by 1970 (Shaw 1979). The average Swedish farm family derived 37 per cent of its income from other sources in 1966, 68 per cent in 1980 (Persson 1983). In France the proportion of farm-household income from non-farm activities and pensions was 30 per cent in 1970, 42 per cent by 1981 (Robson 1987) while the proportion of Japanese farm-household income from off-farm sources rose from 45 per cent in 1960 to 75 per cent by 1979 (Kada 1982a).

THE INCOME CLASSIFICATION

A number of countries make a useful if somewhat arbitrary distinction between part-time farmers who depend mainly on the farm for a living (Class I or part-time main-income farmers) and those mainly dependent on off-farm occupations (Class II or supplementary income farmers). Breakdowns of this type have proved their worth for analysing trends in part-time farming. Depending on what data is available, the classification can be based on working time or income and it can embrace farmers alone, farming couples or farm households. In France and Italy for example, farmers are divided into those with 'prevalent' and 'secondary' off-farm work. In the Netherlands and Belgium the crucial consideration is whether the farm operator spends more than half his working time off the farm or in a non-farm occupation. Canada, the United States and Finland base their definitions on the number of days the operator works off the farm. Germany uses a combination of the farmer's working time and the couple's earned income. Japan has the most comprehensive scheme, dividing the part-time farming households into Type I where net farm income exceeds non-farm income and Type II where non-farm income is the greater (OECD 1978:3–5).

Income rather than time was chosen as the basis for classifying part-time farming families in England and Wales. The terms of reference for the farm survey included measuring the importance of other gainful activities to the *total income* of farm families and income measures seem most relevant for policy goals concerned with farm-family income and welfare. Income measures are being used to an increasing extent in studies of part-time farming in other countries and now that the Inland Revenue is making its Survey of Personal Incomes available for research purposes, more analysis of incomes and income sources of British farmers may be expected (Hill 1987). The farm household was chosen as the unit of analysis for the present study and the notion of the family's combined earnings from all sources seems less artificial than the concept of 'total labour time'. Experience in the pilot study showed, in any case, that the use of time as a yardstick is fraught with difficulties. An hour of work is not a constant unit but varies as between young and old, male and female, experienced and inexperienced workers and between farm and non-farm occupations. Work expands to fill the time allotted to it and nowhere is this more true than for part-time farmers who treat their farming as a form of recreation or an activity for retirement.

PART-TIME FARMING CLASSES IN ENGLAND AND WALES

When asked what was the main source of earned income for the farm household, only 17 of the 700 cooperators in the farm survey, equivalent to 2 per cent of the part-time farming population, declined to reply. Table 6.1 shows that those mainly dependent on farm incomes were outnumbered by those mainly dependent on other sources by about two to one.

Table 6.1 Main source of earned income in part-time farming households

Main source	Estimated numbers	Per cent
Farming	16 393 *b*	31.3
Other sources	33 209 *a*	63.5
Half and half	1 289	2.5
No earnings	330	0.6
No reply	1 124	2.1
All households	52 345	100.0

(*Source*: 1984 farm survey, raised results)

Including all working members of the farm household in the question made little difference. A handful of respondents who had disclosed the main source of the farmer and spouse's earnings were unwilling to answer the question for the farm household. In only eleven cases was the contribution of other members of the household sufficient to swing the balance from farming to other occupations as the main source of earnings and in no case was the swing the other way. The net effect was to raise the proportion of families mainly dependent on other earnings from 62 to 64 per cent. Those who have argued that it is sufficient to take the farmer and spouse's earnings into account when arriving at the main source of farm-household income, could take support from these figures. A word of caution is necessary, however. While just half (124 out of 247) of the households in the sample with other members earning, claimed that those members contributed to the family budget, the other earners were most often sons and daughters making what their parents regarded as a nominal contribution for their keep. Some respondents felt that this amounted to 'contributing earned income', others did not. It is possible that a more consistent approach in the way the question was asked would have produced a slightly different result. As pointed out in Chapter 3, the topic of farm youth and their contribution to the household economy is a neglected one deserving further research.

Replies to the question on the main source of household income enabled farms in the sample to be allocated to Class I or Class II. The 17 cases with no reply were decided easily enough by reference to other information they had given. Twenty respondents who stated that farm and other earnings were the same were put into Class I and those claiming to have no earned income, into Class II. Raising the results to national level gave 18 110 part-time farms in Class I and 34 234 in Class II. For some purposes it proved helpful to subdivide the large Class II into Class IIa, those farms reporting to have made some income from the farm in the latest financial year and Class IIb which had made a loss or only broken even according to their farm accounts. A total of 18 023 farms were thus designated Class IIa and 16 211 Class IIb. The last step in the classification was somewhat questionable in view of the instability of farm incomes from year to year and another year might have produced a different breakdown. Farm incomes in the UK did in fact show a slight upturn in 1984, only to slump again in 1985 to a point 46 per cent lower (Ministry of Agriculture, Fisheries and Food 1987).

The 1984 farm-survey estimate of 64 per cent of part-time farming households mainly dependent on other sources of earned income compares with a figure of 66 per cent for farmers and spouses in the pilot study and 68 per cent for farmers only in Harrison's national study (Harrison (1975:13). In almost all developed countries, it seems, Class II part-time farms outnumber Class I. Canada, like England and Wales, has roughly two part-time farms in Class II to every one in Class I whilst in most other OECD countries the ratio is three to one or even higher (OECD 1978). In Ireland, for example, 88 per cent of part-time farmers who are wage earners are in Class II (Higgins 1983:34).

Table 6.2 shows the expected, highly significant association between size of farm and income class. In band 1, 85 per cent of holdings are in Class II and they are evenly divided between IIa and IIb. Moving up the size spectrum Class I expands and Class II contracts so that in the top size band, three-quarters of the holdings are in Class I. Yet it is clear from the table that size of farm is not the only factor determining the relative importance of farm and non-farm sources of income. A quarter of the holdings in the top size band are in Class II with larger non-farm earnings and a small but significant number in band I still relies mainly on income from farming.

The income classification also discriminates between the main categories of employment in the sense that the class distribution of holdings involved in each main type of activity differs very significantly from that of holdings not involved. More than 60 per cent of

Table 6.2 Distribution of part-time farms by income class and size of holding

Size band	Class I	Class IIa	Class IIb	All holdings
	per cent of part-time holdings			
1	14.8	42.2	43.0	100.0
2	38.7	35.2	26.1	100.0
3	63.1	24.3	12.6	100.0
4	75.3	14.9	9.8	100.0
All holdings	34.6	34.4	31.0	100.0 ***
Numbers	18 110 a	18 023 b	16 211 b	52 344

(*Source*: 1984 farm survey, raised results)

the holdings involved in farm-based enterprises or with household members working on other farms are in Class I where farming at home remains the principal source of income. More than 60 per cent of those involved in off-farm work or home businesses are in Class II and at least a quarter in Class IIb, making no net income from farming in the latest year, as Table 6.3 shows.

Table 6.3 Distribution of part-time farms by income class and type of occupation

Type of activity	Class I	Class IIa	Class IIb	All holdings
	per cent of holdings involved in activity			
Off-farm work	36.4	34.3	29.3	100.0 ***
Home business	32.9	41.6	25.5	100.0 ***
Farm-based enterprise	61.5	21.5	17.0	100.0 ***
Work on other farms	64.6	24.1	11.3	100.0 ***

(*Source*: 1984 farm survey, sample results)

Class II part-time farms outnumber Class I in every region of England and Wales. The north of England and East Anglia stand out in Fig. 6.1 as the two regions where part-time farming families are most dependent on the farming side but even here, Class II is larger. Dependence on other income sources is highest in the most

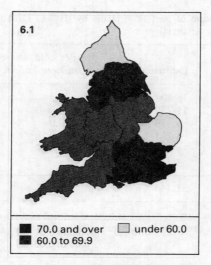

6.1

| 70.0 and over | under 60.0 |
| 60.0 to 69.9 | |

Fig. 6.1 Percentage of part-time farms in Class II by region.

urbanised regions, the north-west, south-east and Yorkshire/Humberside regions each having more than 70 per cent of their part-time farms in Class II. (Regional differences in the class distribution of part-time farms just missed significance at the 10 per cent level, however.)

INCOMES FROM FARMING

Respondents in the 1984 farm survey were asked to indicate a band corresponding to their taxable income from farming in the latest year for which figures were available. From their replies it was estimated that 38 per cent of all part-time farms had made a loss or only broken even on their farming activities in the last financial year and that nearly two-thirds had made less than £2000 before tax. Only 8 per cent had made farm incomes of £10 000 or more. To put the figures in Table 6.4 into context, 1983/4 was a bad year for farm incomes generally. In fact 200 of the 700 farmers taking part in the survey claimed that the year in question had been exceptional. These respondents were clustered at the ends of the income range with 44 per cent of them making a loss; some would expect to make a reasonable income from farming in most years.

Self-reported information on personal incomes is bound to be treated with a degree of scepticism. Cooperators in the farm survey were not pressed to disclose details of their private incomes if they

Table 6.4 Distribution of part-time farms by level of farm income reported for latest financial year

Farm income £000s	Estimated numbers	Per cent where income known	Per cent in pilot study
Loss or nil	18 401 *b*	38.3	37.2
Under 2.0	11 779 *b*	24.5	25.3†
2.0 to 4.9	9 633 *c*	20.0	26.0†
5.0 to 9.9	4 281	8.9	6.9
10.0 and over	4 040	8.3	4.6
Not disclosed	4 210	–	–
All holdings	52 344	100.0	100.0

(*Source*: 1984 farm survey, raised results and pilot study).
† Income bands in the pilot study were under £1000 and £1000 to £4999.

did not wish to and no attempt was made to cross-question them or to check up on the information they volunteered. The figures can therefore only be taken at face value. Only 58 out of 700 did not answer the question on farm incomes including some who were genuinely willing but unable to do so because farming and other activities were not separated in their accounts. There may well have been a temptation to understate income, especially if the question was associated in the respondent's mind with taxation but equally some respondents may have overstated the profitability of their farms in order to impress the interviewer. As an independent check of a sort, results from the pilot study which used a different sample are also presented in Table 6.4. Although different income bands were used the overall income distribution is not out of line with that obtained in 1984.

Respondents were asked for farm income before tax which was believed to be an easily accessible figure and one that would be readily understood. It may not be the most satisfactory measure of disposable income for the farm household, particularly where a large amount is being reinvested in the business or where the farm has to support more than one household. An estimated 13 per cent of part-time farming households had partners or directors living in separate dwellings. Usually these partners were parents of the farmer or his wife or sometimes brothers or sisters who had inherited a share in the family business. In many cases they were sleeping partners and they did not necessarily draw an income from the farm. Having non-household partners was a feature of the largest, most profitable farm businesses, it was associated with Class I households and it was considerably more common in East Anglia and the north of England than elsewhere; all these relationships were highly significant. The proportion of farms with non-household partners rose from 7 per cent among farms making a loss to 34 per cent where farm income had exceeded £10 000.

Table 6.5 illustrates a predictably close relationship between the level of farm income and holding size. Nearly half the part-time holdings in band 1 (under 100 smd) claimed to have made a loss or no income from farming in the latest financial year as against only one in six in the top size band (500 smd and over). Farm incomes of £5000 or more were reported by fewer than 5 per cent of farmers in band 1 but by 57 per cent in band 4.

Table 6.5 Level of farm income by size of holding

Farm income £000s	Size band	1	2	3	4	All holdings
		per cent of holdings where income known				
Loss or nil		47.9	35.6	27.2	16.2	38.3
Under 2.0		31.8	21.9	13.2	10.6	24.5
2.0 to 4.9		15.4	31.8	28.0	16.2	20.0
5.0 and over		4.9	10.7	31.6	57.0	17.2
All holdings		100.0	100.0	100.0	100.0	100.0 ***

(*Source*: 1984 farm survey, raised results)

More than half the part-time farms in the south-east of England and 44 per cent in the West Midlands had made no net contribution to the household income in the latest year, including some cases where this was a deliberate policy. Few part-time farms in north-west England reported farm income above £5000 either. The most profitable farms, according to Fig. 6.2, were to be found in the north of England and East Anglia, the two regions which seem to be the most farm oriented. (In this case regional differences were significant at the 5 per cent level.)

Households which combine farming with off-farm work or a home business tend towards the lower levels of farm income, according to Table 6.6. Those involved with off-farm work had significantly lower farm incomes than those not involved. More than a third of them stated that farming had made no financial contribution to household

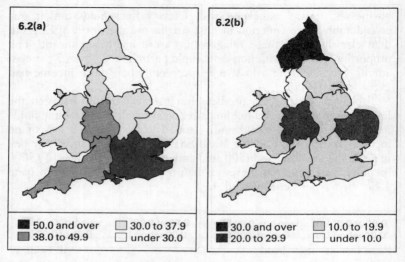

Fig. 6.2 Regional variations in farm income.
    (a) Percentage of part-time farms making a loss or no taxable income from farming in last financial year.
    (b) Percentage of part-time farms making £5000 or more taxable income from farming in last financial year.

Table 6.6 Level of farm income by nature of other activity

Farm income £000s	Home business	Off-farm work	Farm-based enterprise	Work on other farms
	per cent where farm income known			
Loss	20.4	19.6	18.1	11.1
Nil/broke even	13.9	17.1	11.3	6.3
Under 2.0	17.5	19.6	14.4	15.9
2.0 to 4.9	27.0	21.3	25.5	24.4
5.0 to 9.9	12.4	11.1	16.9	23.8
10.0 and over	8.8	11.3	13.8	18.5
All holdings	100.0	100.0	100.0	100.0
	ns	**	ns	***

(*Source*: 1984 farm survey, sample results)

cash income in the latest year, including some who for tax reasons were anxious to show a loss on their farming accounts. At the other extreme, households involved with work on other farms made significantly *higher* farm incomes than the rest with nearly one in five reporting a pre-tax income of over £10 000 and only 17 per cent not showing a profit. Holdings supporting farm-based enterprises came in between.

The figures in Table 6.7, based on the smaller pilot study sample, tell a similar story but shed more light on the relationship between farmers' incomes from farming and the nature of their other occupations. Those in the higher paid salaried professions, administrative and executive positions were the most likely to declare a loss or to claim that they made no income out of farming. In the pilot sample 15 per cent of them claimed to have made a loss and 60 per cent no net income from the farm in the previous year. Farmer-businessmen ran much more profitable farms as a rule, their performance being close to that of farmers with farm-based enterprises who usually relied mainly on the farm for their livelihood. Farmers whose other jobs were in the manual and service sectors came in between; few could afford to make a loss but few made large profits from farming either. Nearly half of them claimed that the farm did not contribute to their current income so presumably they were not paying tax on farm profits.

Table 6.7 Level of farm income and nature of farmers' other work

Farm income £000s	Prof/admin/ executive	Service/ manual	Non-farm business	Farm-based enterprise	Work on other farms	Total
	per cent of farmers					
Loss	15.2	8.3	8.0	6.0	3.8	8.2
Nil/broke even	42.4	40.2	26.0	25.0	15.4	29.0
Under 1.0	22.7	27.8	32.0	27.4	23.1	25.3
1.0 to 4.9	15.2	19.5	18.0	32.1	42.4	26.0
5.0 and over	4.5	4.2	16.0	9.5	15.3	11.5
All farmers	100.0	100.0	100.0	100.0	100.0	100.0
Numbers	66	72	50	84	52	392

(*Source*: pilot study)

OTHER EARNINGS

Part-time farming families' earnings from other activities were on average higher and often very much higher than their incomes from farming. From the farm survey it was estimated that over half the households had other earned incomes in excess of £5000 and that 36 per cent were earning £10 000 or more from their other activities; only 8 per cent made as much from farming. Only 22 per cent claimed to have earned less than £2000 from other sources in the latest year while three times that number said that they had made less than £2000 from their farms (Table 6.8). The distribution of other incomes in the pilot study, also shown in the table, was of the same order. The lapse of three years between the two surveys would help to account for pilot-study incomes being pitched at a lower level.

Table 6.8 Distribution of part-time farms by level of household earnings from other sources in latest financial year

Income level £000s	Estimated numbers	Per cent where income known	Per cent in pilot study
Under 2.0	9 332 b	21.8	26.2†
2.0 to 4.9	8 572 b	20.0	27.2†
5.0 to 9.9	9 253 b	22.3	23.3
10.0 and over	15 593 b	35.9	23.3
Not disclosed	9 594 b	–	–
All holdings	52 344	100.0	100.0

(*Source*: 1984 farm survey, raised results and pilot study)
† Income bands in the pilot study were under £1000 and £1000 to £4999.

Respondents were noticeably more reticent about other earnings than about their incomes from farming. A total of 125 were unwilling or unable to divulge the level of earnings from other sources in the latest year compared with only 58 non-responses to the question on farm incomes. A further 31 claimed that the household had received no income from other sources in the twelve months prior to the survey. It will be recalled that the sample was drawn from holdings reporting another paid job for the farmer or spouse in the twelve months ended June 1983 whereas the farm survey covered the period June 1983 to June 1984. Including non-farm earnings of other household members had the effect of increasing the number of cases (from 106 to 125) where the income level was not disclosed, reducing numbers of households with no other earnings and those earning less than £2000 and increasing numbers with combined earnings of over £10 000

Highest non-farm earnings are associated with the smallest holdings. As Table 6.9 shows, the proportion of holdings earning less than £2000 from other sources rose from 13 per cent in band 1 to 40 per cent in band 4. Whilst the proportion earning over £10 000 was highest in band 1 (44 per cent) and decreased with increasing farm size, there is some suggestion in Table 6.9 of the proportion with high non-farm earnings beginning to rise again beyond band 3. The pilot study demonstrated the trend more clearly, highest non-farm earnings being associated with the smallest and the largest part-time farms.

Table 6.9 Level of non-farm earnings by size of holding

Income levels £000s	Size band	1	2	3	4	All holdings
	per cent of holdings where income known					
Under 2.0		13.2	25.7	31.4	39.5	21.8
2.0 to 4.9		18.6	17.0	28.1	21.8	20.0
5.0 to 9.9		24.2	24.6	17.0	13.2	22.3
10.0 and over		44.0	32.7	23.5	25.5	35.9
All holdings		100.0	100.0	100.0	100.0	100.0 ***

(*Source*: 1984 farm survey, raised results)

This discovery of a U-shaped distribution of non-farm incomes according to farm size is by no means unique or confined to England and Wales. Buttel (1982) and Hill (1987) have commented on the phenomenon in the United States and it was previously noted in the OECD study:

> In areas where off-farm employment is available, a large percentage of farmers with non-viable holdings receive earned income from other sources: this income is comparable to that earned by normal wage earners in the district and is the dominant source of income received by the farm household. With increasing farm size, until the viable family farm size is reached, it is found that the percentage of farmers with off-farm work declines, as also does the average income from this off-farm work. Off-farm employment, as well as income from this employment, then tend to rise slowly as the size groups above the family farm are reached (OECD 1978:24).

Non-farm earnings vary significantly between the regions. According to Fig. 6.3, more than 40 per cent of all part-time farming

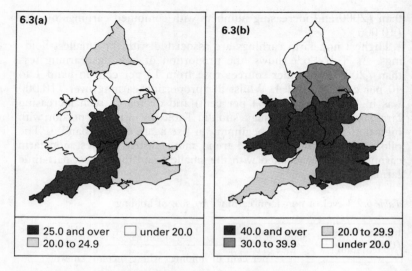

Fig. 6.3 Regional variations in non-farm earnings.
   (a) Percentage of part-time farms with other earnings of less than
      £2000 in last financial year.
   (b) Percentage of part-time farms with other earnings of £10 000
      or more in last financial year.

households in south-east England, the Midlands and Wales were earning £10 000 or more from other activities in the survey period. East Anglia and the north of England, the most farm-oriented regions, had the fewest farm households in this income bracket. The pilot study also revealed a strong tendency for non-farm earnings to decline with increasing distance from urban centres. One-third of the households in the most urbanised areas but only 13 per cent in the most rural, were earning £10 000 or more from non-farm sources.

Highest non-farm incomes are earned in off-farm occupations. Table 6.10 shows that 40 per cent of holdings in this occupational category had outside earnings of £10 000 or more and this was a significantly larger proportion than in other households. Households with home businesses came next, 37 per cent of them earning £10 000 or more from outside agriculture. Farm families with farm-based enterprises had the lowest non-farm earnings, 42 per cent of them making less than £2000 in the latest year and only 21 per cent more than £10 000. Their non-farm earnings were in fact significantly *lower*

Table 6.10 Level of non-farm earnings by nature of other activity

Income level £000s	Off-farm work	Home business	Work on other farms	Farm-based enterprise
	per cent of holdings where income known			
Under 2.0	15.4	15.3	29.6	41.7
2.0 to 4.9	20.4	25.8	24.5	22.0
5.0 to 9.9	24.0	21.8	18.9	15.8
10.0 and over	40.2	37.1	27.0	20.5
All holdings	100.0	100.0	100.0	100.0
	***	**	***	***

(*Source*: 1984 farm survey, sample results)

than those of other households. Families involved in work on other farms, the group with highest average farm incomes, did not have the lowest incomes from other sources; 27 per cent of them were in the top income bracket in Table 6.10.

More detailed analysis in the pilot study revealed a close link between earnings and status of the non-farm job. Highest earnings were associated with high-status professional, administrative and managerial posts. More junior posts within the same broad occupational categories came next in the earnings league. Lowest non-farm earnings went with service occupations, manual jobs being on the whole rather better paid. Farmers running their own non-farm businesses came in between. These results need to be compared with those in Table 6.7 which suggested a large proportion of part-time farmers in professional, administrative and executive posts showing a loss on their farms. Supporting evidence comes from Ireland where part-time farmers with professional and other salaried occupations similarly had the highest non-farm earnings (Higgins 1983).

TRAVEL TO WORK

Although part-time farmers with off-farm jobs appeared to be earning the most from outside farming they probably had to cover the highest costs in travelling to work. The average time and cost of a journey to work is likely to be higher for part-time farmers than for urban dwellers. In isolated rural areas the cost might even outweigh the benefits of another paid job. The pilot study therefore sought information on farmers' and spouses' journeys to off-farm jobs. It was assumed that farm and home-based businesses and work on other farms would only involve short local journeys.

It emerged that 40 per cent of journeys to off-farm jobs were up to 5 miles (8 km) and 68 per cent up to 10 miles (16 km). Fewer than 20 per cent of journeys were of 20 miles (32 km) or more. Taking into account shorter journeys for those working at home or on other farms it can be assumed that most part-time farmers do not have to face excessively long journeys to work. In the Irish study similarly 85 per cent of part-time farmers who were wage workers travelled no more than 10 miles (16 km) to work, the average distance being only $6\frac{1}{2}$ miles (10 km) (Higgins 1983:38).

Table 6.11 suggests that farmers were, on the whole, prepared to travel further to engage in the better paid, higher status occupations. Whilst 40 per cent of farmers with professional occupations travelled 20 miles (32 km) or more, only 6 per cent travelled as far for manual jobs. Over half the journeys to service and manual jobs but under a third for professional and 'big business' jobs were no more than 5 miles. This association was highly significant for both farmers and spouses. The pilot study also established that farmers travelled greater distances to main jobs than to subsidiary jobs; 40 per cent of trips to main jobs but only 17 per cent to subsidiary jobs exceeded 10 miles. Surprisingly, however, Louisiana farmers and wives commuted considerably *further* to blue-collar than to white-collar jobs (Deseran forthcoming).

Table 6.11 Distance farmers travel to work by nature of off-farm occupation

Nature of occupation	Distance in miles:				All journeys
	Up to 5	6 to 10	11 to 20	Over 20	
	per cent of farmers' journeys				
Profession	25.7	22.9	11.4	40.0	100.0
Large business	30.9	21.5	19.1	28.5	100.0
Small business	43.9	26.8	22.0	7.3	100.0
Service	53.0	35.3	–	11.7	100.0
Manual	51.0	35.3	7.8	5.9	100.0
All journeys	40.3	28.0	13.4	18.3	100.0 ***
Numbers	75	52	25	34	186

(*Source*: pilot study)

The Louisiana and pilot studies agreed that farmers travel greater distances to off-farm jobs than their wives do. Under 5 per cent of farmers in the pilot study but 13 per cent of spouses worked within a 2 mile (3 km) radius of home. As Deseran has pointed out, it is not only the cost of the journey but the time involved which is likely to deter wives from commuting long distances since taking a job off the farm will not, in most cases, free them from responsibilities of preparing meals, looking after the children and performing numerous chores on the farm.

Deseran has suggested that the labour market for farm women is severely constrained by their restricted commuting behaviour. The pilot study found that women not only travelled shorter distances to work than men did but also used different means of transport. In the sample 70 per cent of farmers but only 55 per cent of spouses with off-farm jobs used their own cars to drive to work. For a further 5 per cent of farmers but only 1 per cent of spouses the job itself involved driving – a van, bus or lorry or, in one case, a hearse. More spouses than farmers walked or cycled to work, waited for lifts or used public transport, the last accounting for 2 per cent of farmers' and 11 per cent of spouses' journeys.

As Deseran suggests, farm women's commuting ability could act as a constraint on their employment opportunities. A farmer's wife without a car might be limited to jobs within walking or cycling distance of the farm, a radius of one or two miles (up to 3 km), which would restrict her choice very considerably. On the other hand, it is possible that the commuting behaviour of women could be determined *by* job opportunities. If a farmer's wife were qualified, as some of them are, to take a job as a head teacher or matron of a hospital, she could afford to run a car and commute a greater distance in order to take up a suitable post.

Wimberley (1983) has argued that off-farm employment opportunities for members of US farm families depend more upon the availability of employment within reasonable commuting distance from the farm than upon a willingness to move closer to the job. While this is no doubt generally true in Britain as well, results of the pilot study seem to imply a rather more active stance for farmers and their families. A direct link seems to exist between the distance that members of farm families are prepared to commute to off-farm jobs and the rewards obtained. Longer journeys are felt to be justified for main jobs and for higher paid jobs with more status attached. Assuming the location of the farm to be fixed, it is possible to visualise members of farm households trading off non-farm earnings against the distance and cost of a journey to work. But equally the off-farm job could be taken as the fixed point with the position of the farm and the journey to work allowed to vary. In that case those with the highest paid non-farm jobs could afford to travel furthest in search of the most desirable farms.

TOTAL HOUSEHOLD INCOMES

Whereas part-time farmers of two or three generations ago used to be considered among the poorest strata in rural society, they are now among the wealthiest. Krasovec (1977) backed up this view with evidence from Yugoslavia and Poland, Germany, France and Belgium, the United Kingdom, Ireland and Japan. In Yugoslavia the regions with a high proportion of part-time farming households are now among the most prosperous. Greater purchasing power on the part of the farming population boosts demand for consumer goods and building materials, leading in turn to a growth in employment. The OECD report concluded that through off-farm employment the total income of part-time farming families often compares favourably with that earned on much bigger full-time farms. One consequence is that expenditure on the farmhouse and on household amenities as well as on farm machinery can be relatively high on part-time farms. Cawley (1983) found this to be the case in Galway where additional income from the off-farm work was helping to erode income differences between full-time and part-time farms. Higgins (1983:35) estimated that average total earnings of Irish part-time farmers and spouses who were wage earners were one-third greater than the average farm-family income of full-time farmers in 1981. These part-time farmers were able to earn more than the average industrial wage too, with the added security of the farm to fall back on in case of unemployment. In Japan, always the extreme case, off-farm earnings have not only equalised incomes within agriculture but raised the per capita income of the entire farming population above the non-farm (Kada 1982b:313).

Total incomes of most part-time farming families in England and Wales appear to be adequate. Table 6.12, based on survey cases providing complete income information, estimates the level of farm and other earnings for the whole part-time farming population. Altogether 68 per cent of household reported earning at least £5000 from one source in the latest year and a further 5 per cent had earned between £4000 and £10 000 from two sources combined. The top income bands were open-ended and some of those who declared that they had earned more than £5000 from farming or more than £10 000 from other activities had very large incomes indeed.

One large group in Table 6.12 was the 17 per cent of households making no income from farming but earning £10 000 or more from other sources. A total of 42 per cent of households had off-farm

Table 6.12 Distribution of part-time farming households by level of farm and other earnings in latest financial year

Farm income £000s	Earnings from other sources in £000s				
	Under 2.0	2.0 to 4.9	5.0 to 9.9	10.0 and over	
	per cent of holdings where income known				Total
Loss/nil	5.6	6.7	9.0	17.0	38.3
Under 2.0	4.7	4.4	7.3	8.3	24.7
2.0 to 4.9	5.3	5.1	3.2	7.3	20.9
5.0 and over	5.7	4.1	2.2	4.1	16.1
All holdings	21.3	20.3	21.7	36.7	100.0 **

(*Source*: 1984 farm survey, raised results)

incomes of at least £5000 coupled with low farm incomes. Not all of those with low incomes from one source had compensating high earnings from elsewhere, however. From a welfare point of view attention should be paid to the 10 per cent of part-time farming households claiming to have made less than £2000 from their farms *and* less than £2000 from other activities in the latest year.

Instability of farm incomes means that some of those with low incomes in one year could expect to make a reasonable return at other times. As Table 6.13 suggests. 18 per cent of those with farming losses in the year in question were mainly dependent on farming for their living in an average year. Relatively few of the households

Table 6.13 Level of income and dependence on income source

Farm income £000s	Per cent mainly dependent on farm income	Other earnings £000s	Per cent mainly dependent on other income source
Loss	18.4		
Nil/broke even	27.2	Nil	8.1
Under 2.0	32.3	Under 2.0	7.5
2.0 to 4.9	51.0	2.0 to 4.9	43.5
5.0 to 9.9	80.8	5.0 to 9.9	71.0
10.0 and over	89.5 ***	10.0 and over	88.2 ***

(*Source*: 1984 farm survey, sample results)

reporting off-farm earnings of less than £2000 were mainly dependent on them, however.

Households reporting low incomes from farming and other activities might have other unearned sources of income. Ashton and Cracknell (1961) found that 14 per cent of the occupiers of holdings below 250 smd had pensions or private incomes but no other paid occupation. To explore this possibility the farm survey asked whether members of the household were in receipt of income from other sources such as pensions, rents or investments. Only 263 respondents (37 per cent of the sample) admitted to having any unearned income. Response to this question was very guarded, farmers being understandably reluctant to discuss unearned incomes. The results therefore need to be treated with caution and any conclusions must be tentative.

Nearly half the families reporting any unearned income claimed to be receiving less than £2000 per annum which is less than the state Old Age Pension for a couple. Only 17 per cent admitted to receiving more than £5000 from pensions, rents or investments. Largest unearned incomes tended to go with the largest farms and the lowest incomes from other paid work. The survey identified just 31 households, under 5 per cent of the sample, with unearned incomes greater than their farm incomes or their earnings from other sources. All but one was receiving more than £2000 per annum in pensions, rent or interest payments. These households tended to be concentrated in the lower income brackets for both farming and other activities. Existence of unearned incomes must, therefore, help to mitigate the financial situation for some part-time farming families with low incomes.

Not all the families facing financial hardship were in receipt of unearned incomes, however. Whilst households mainly dependent on unearned incomes were mostly clustered in band 1, low earnings were more characteristic of middle-sized farms than of the smallest or largest. Holdings in band 2 (100 to 250 smd) account for 18 per cent of all part-time farms but 25 per cent of those with combined earnings of less than £4000. Band 3 (250 to 500 smd) includes 13 per cent of all part-time holdings but 21 per cent of those with the lowest earnings. This seems to imply that the most severe income problems are related to holdings which are too small to yield an adequate income from farming alone yet too large to allow the farmer to take another full-time job.

Four-fifths of the households with the lowest incomes were in Class I with farming the main activity and source of income. A natural response in these circumstances would be for the farmer or his wife to start another enterprise on the farm, bed-and-breakfast being an obvious example. Comparing Tables 6.6 and 6.10 shows that the households carrying farm-based enterprises tend to have the lowest incomes from other activities but not necessarily high incomes from farming. In fact, holdings involved in farm-based enterprises had a disproportionate share of low incomes. The south-west region, where farm-based enterprises are prevalent, had 21 per cent of all part-time farms but 32 per cent of those with the lowest incomes. North-west England, the south-east and the West Midlands also had more than their share.

In conclusion, part-time farming does seem to be the answer for many families living on holdings which are too small to provide a reasonable living. While most are believed to have total household incomes from all sources which are adequate. and some much more than adequate, a minority do not seem able to generate sufficient income by combining other activities with farming. Their concentration on holdings which are too large for spare-time working suggests that it may be the organisation of the farm itself which prevents the farmer from taking a better paid off-farm job. The next chapter therefore turns to farms and farming systems.

Farming systems and performance

The focus of this chapter is the part-time farm, its size and type, its performance and propensity to change. It will be seen that part-time farms are generally small, operating along simple lines with an inbuilt resistance to change. Those farms providing the major share of household income differ in every respect from those where farm income is subsidiary. An underlying question which the present study cannot answer is whether it is the existence of another occupation which determines the structure and performance of part-time farms or vice versa.

SIZE OF PART-TIME FARMS

Part-time farms are predominantly small. The total area of holdings where farmers and/or spouses have other paid jobs was estimated from the farm survey to be just over two million hectares, slightly more than one-sixth of the total agricultural area of England and Wales. The average size of part-time holdings is estimated to be 38.5 ha compared with 72.3 ha for full-time farms. The position in Ireland is not dissimilar, part-time farms accounting for 15.4 per cent of the land farmed. Average farm sizes there are much smaller, part-time holdings averaging only 13.8 ha and full-time 23.3 ha (Higgins 1983:73).

It was no surprise to find the largest part-time farms in East Anglia (average size 62 ha) and the north of England (53 ha) in line with the strong farming orientation in those regions. The smallest part-time holdings were in the north-west region, averaging only 22 ha, which may have been due to a number of glasshouse holdings being included in the sample there.

The OECD study found that Class II part-time farms were concentrated in the smallest size groups. In Austria, Germany, Norway and Japan, for example, Class II part-time farms were on average only about one-third the size of full-time farms (OECD 1978:11). Table 7.1 suggests that in England and Wales those part-time holdings designated Class IIb are only about a third the size of full-time farms. A surprising discovery is that Class I holdings are on average slightly *larger* than full-time farms over the country as a whole.

Table 7.1 Average size of part-time holdings by income class

Income class	Mean area per holding ha	Mean area farmed ha
Class I	79.8	85.9
Class IIa	33.7	38.2
Class IIb	24.3	25.1
All holdings	38.5 (sd 77.6)[†]	41.2 (sd 85.0)[†]

(*Source*: 1984 farm survey, raised results for totals only)
[†] Differences between sample means for Class I, Class IIa and Class IIb are statistically significant but standard errors are large, reflecting the considerable degree of variation within the sample

The total area *farmed* by occupiers of part-time holdings was estimated to be some 7 per cent greater than the total area of their holdings. The average area actually farmed was 41.2 ha as against an average holding size of 38.5 ha. The main reason is that the area of land rented by part-time farmers on a seasonal or short-term basis exceeds the area which they let seasonally to other farmers. The net effect of seasonal and short-term tenancies is to redistribute land from the smaller to the larger part-time farms since occupiers in bands 1 and 2 were found to be net renters out while those in bands 3 and 4 were net renters in. Table 7.1 suggests that land is redistributed between main living and supplementary income farms since Class IIb added only 0.8 ha on average while Class I rented an additional 6.1 ha. The inference must be that for some part-time farmers in Class II, owning land is more important than farming it while the reverse is generally true for Class I.

TENURE OF PART-TIME HOLDINGS

Owner occupation is more important in part-time than full-time farms, suggesting again that some part-time farmers may be more interested in owning land than farming it. The pilot study found that two-thirds of part-time holdings were wholly owned by their occupiers as compared with under half of all agricultural holdings in England and Wales at that time. From the 1984 farm survey it was possible to estimate the total area of land in part-time farms held under different forms of tenure. As Table 7.2 shows, 66 per cent of the land is owner-occupied which compares with 60 per cent for all holdings in England and Wales in 1984. A further 28 per cent in part-time holdings is rented under normal agricultural tenancies which leaves just under 6 per cent held under other tenure forms such as landlord–tenant partnerships and renting 'at less than arm's length' from a member of the family.

Table 7.2 Land tenure in part-time holdings

Tenure form	Estimated area 000s ha	Per cent of area
Owner-occupied	1 326	65.8
Rented under normal agricultural tenancies	568	28.2
Other tenures	120	6.0
All holdings	2 013	100.0

(*Source*: 1984 farm survey, raised results)

Owner occupation is more widespread on Welsh than English farms with 72 per cent of the total agricultural area of Wales and only 58 per cent in England owner-occupied in 1984. Part-time farming follows the same pattern with 79 per cent of the agricultural area on Welsh part-time farms owner-occupied. Figure 7.1 also suggests that owner occupation is more prevalent on part-time farms in the south of England than in the east, Midlands or north. Again this seems to indicate a stronger investment motive among part-time farmers in the south of England.

The less important farming is in relation to total household income and employment, the larger the share of land that is owned. According to Table 7.3, Class IIb farmers in the sample owned 79 per cent of

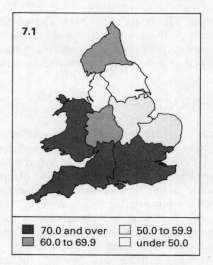

7.1

■ 70.0 and over	□ 50.0 to 59.9
▨ 60.0 to 69.9	□ under 50.0

Fig. 7.1 Percentage of owner-occupied land in part-time farms.

the land they occupied, Class I only 63 per cent. Renting under normal agricultural tenancies is more likely to occur where farming is the main source of income, almost a third of the Class I land being held in this way. The practice of renting at less than arm's length is most common in Class IIa. The tenure pattern seems to reflect the importance of owning land in families where the farming occupation is secondary. For those farming for a living and, by implication, under pressure to increase the area farmed in order to maintain their incomes, it has been more cost-effective to rent than to purchase extra

Table 7.3 Tenure of land in part-time holdings by income class

Tenure form	Class I	Class IIa	Class IIb
	per cent of total holding area		
Owner-occupied	63.2	71.0	79.1
Rented under normal agricultural tenancies	32.0	16.7	17.8
Other tenures	4.8	12.3	3.1
All holdings	100.0	100.0	100.0

(*Source*: 1984 farm survey, sample results)

land in recent years. The relationship between part-time farming and owner occupation may also say something about the attitude of landowners towards part-time farmers and particularly towards those who are less experienced or not wholly committed to farming for profit.

TYPES OF FARMING

Part-time farmers in general operate on a smaller scale than full-timers, they have less time available for farming and they are not under the same pressure to maximise or even to maintain their farm incomes. These tendencies are reflected in their choice of enterprises. Part-time farmers tend to favour simpler and less demanding systems than those who depend on farming for their livelihood.

On the arable side, part-time farming often means a shift away from the more labour-demanding crops towards labour-extensive ones like cereals. Cereal production is relatively important on part-time farms in the United States, Germany and Norway, for example (OECD 1978:11). In a mixed farming area included in the Kent and East Sussex survey in the mid-1960s, part-time farmers tended to grow cereals while their full-time farming neighbours put more of their acreage under fruit and other high-value crops (Gasson 1966:35). In Japan part-time farmers have specialised in a single cropping of rice, this crop accounting for 54 per cent of gross sales on Class II part-time farms, 29 per cent on Class I and 17 per cent on full-time farms in 1979. Winter crops have been abandoned with the growth of part-time farming (Kada 1982a:370).

Dairy cows are often the first to go in the change from full-time to part-time farming since dairying is a very labour-demanding activity and success depends to a considerable extent on the herdsman's constant vigilance. In some cases it is the abandonment of milk production, precipitated perhaps by the farmer's ill health, labour problems or, more recently, milk quotas, which causes the switch to part-time farming. Part-time farmers in south-east England (Gasson 1966), Wisconsin (Kada 1980), Canada (Bollman 1982), Norway (Symes 1982), southern Sweden (Persson 1983) and Ireland (Higgins 1983) were much less likely than their full-time counterparts to keep dairy cows. In Galway the average size of herds was much smaller on part-time than full-time farms, 76 per cent of part-time farmers who were in milk production keeping no more than 5 cows (Cawley 1983).

Beef production is well suited to the part-time farm and an obvious replacement for the dairy enterprise, being less demanding of time and less critical in its management requirements. In Wisconsin there were many examples of part-time farmers changing from a dairy operation to beef or cash grains (Kada 1980:102). Beef was the most common livestock activity on rural retreats in the Armidale area of New South Wales, being reported on 74 per cent of holdings (McQuin 1978:66). In Ireland an estimated 69 per cent of part-time farmers but only 49 per cent of full timers had a drystock (beef or sheep) enterprise (Higgins 1983:26).

Although the general tendency is towards extensive systems there are examples of part-time farmers successfully combining some highly specialised, labour-intensive enterprise with another job. Success may lie in substituting capital and technical inputs for labour. In the Kent and East Sussex study, for instance, a number of part-time farmers were keeping poultry under highly automated systems which enabled them to be absent from the holding during the day. That survey found that beef cattle, sheep and poultry were all more common on part-time than full-time farms (Gasson 1966:36). Poultry and cattle was the most popular combination of enterprises on holdings below 250 smd in England and Wales in 1955 (Ashton and Cracknell 1961:480). In Canada farmers who produced fruit, vegetables and cattle were the most likely to have worked off the farm during 1975 and in earlier years poultry farmers had also been high on the list (Bollman 1982:314–16).

Crops like grapes, citrus, olives and other orchard crops require most attention for short concentrated periods. With good management such enterprises may be combined with off-farm work. There are apple growers in Kent who have other full-time employment, taking their annual holidays when it is time to pick the crop. Among the wine-growing regions of Yugoslavia there are areas specialising in grapes, peaches, cherries and salad crops. Here the farm family works less than fifty days per year on the holding yet the land is fully utilised all the year round (Krasovec 1983:13).

The latest findings fit in with this broad picture. Cattle and sheep are the mainstay of part-time farms in England and Wales. Table 7.4, derived from the 1983 LII, classifies more than half the holdings where the farmer has another job as cattle and sheep farms. Nearly 60 per cent of holdings where farming is the minor activity come under this heading, as compared with 38 per cent of full-time farms. The table also confirms that dairying is rarely compatible with part-time farming since it is the main enterprise on only 4 per cent of holdings where farming is secondary but 24 per cent where the farmer has no other job. According to the 1983 LII, part-time farmers were neither more nor less likely than full timers to run cropping farms but slightly more likely to specialise in horticulture and slightly less likely to have mixed farms.

Holdings in the 1984 farm survey were classified according to the respondent's description of the main type of farming. This was a rough-and-ready method which would not necessarily produce the

Table 7.4 Type of farming and farmer's main activity

| Type of farming | Farmers with other jobs | | Farmers without other jobs |
	major	minor	
	per cent of holdings		
Dairying	4.1	7.3	23.5
Cattle and sheep	59.7	52.9	37.5
Pigs and poultry	4.1	3.9	3.6
Cropping	21.0	20.6	21.5
Horticulture	6.1	8.0	5.2
Mixed	5.0	7.3	8.7
All types	100.0	100.0	100.0

(*Source*: provisional results of 1983 LII)

same results as the Ministry's classification scheme which is based on detailed cropping and stocking information. Although cattle and sheep farms again appeared to be the most numerous, the dairy enterprise was more prominent in the farm survey than suggested in Table 7.4. The explanation could be that the farm survey included, but Table 7.4 excluded, holdings where the spouse but not the farmer had another job and some of these would be dairy farms.

The farm survey identified some holdings, equivalent to over 10 per cent of all part-time farms in the country, on which there was little or no commercial farming activity. In some cases the land was let on short-term grazing tenancies or the only enterprise was the grazing of horses which are not reckoned to be productive agricultural livestock. Some were subsistence smallholdings with no predominant enterprise but often including sheep, calves, goats, assorted poultry and market-garden crops. Other holdings were found to be used entirely for non-agricultural purposes such as riding schools or caravan parks, or simply left derelict.

Type of farming varied in a predictable and significant way between the regions. The sample classified 70 per cent of holdings in East Anglia and over a third in the East Midlands and Yorkshire/Humberside regions as arable. Almost half the part-time farms in the south-east were arable or horticultural and horticulture was also important in the east and north-west. Dairying was more common in the north and west than elsewhere while cattle and sheep farms accounted for nearly two-thirds of all part-time farms in Wales and almost half in the north and north-west of England.

Type of farming also varies significantly by size of holding and between the income classes. Nearly half the smallest Class IIb holdings specialised in cattle and sheep and nearly half the rest were given over to grazing or non-commercial uses. Holdings in Class IIa put rather less emphasis on cattle, sheep and pasture, rather more on cropping, horticulture and dairying. The pattern was repeated in Class I, these larger part-time farms more often specialising in milk or arable production, less often in cattle, sheep or grazing, pigs, poultry or horticulture (Table 7.5).

Table 7.5 Type of farming by income class

Type of farming	Class I	Class IIa	Class IIb
	per cent of holdings		
Dairying	26.3	8.7	6.1
Cattle and sheep	26.6	45.7	48.9
Arable and mixed	34.8	19.4	6.8
Horticulture	5.7	13.1	8.0
Grazing	3.0	6.8	16.0
Pigs, poultry and other	3.6	6.3	14.2
All holdings	100.0	100.0	100.0 ***

(*Source*: 1984 farm survey, sample results)

The type of farming is also associated with the nature of the other occupation, according to Table 7.6. Holdings with farm-based enterprises are significantly more likely than others to specialise in dairying. Work on other farms is linked with arable and mixed farming and off-farm occupations with cattle and sheep production. Only home businesses are not distinguished by any particular type of farming. While these associations appear to be quite strong, the direction of causality is open to question; does a given type of farming lead to the other activity or vice versa?

With the off-farm work/cattle and sheep combination it is plausible to argue that the other occupation would dictate the choice of farm enterprise. Off-farm work is usually full-time paid employment providing the main source of household income and, as will be seen in Chapter 8, is likely to have come first chronologically. An extensive enterprise like grazing cattle or sheep would not make heavy demands on the farmer's time. It might also be valued for adding to the amenities of the holding. One Australian hobby farmer was quoted as saying 'I bought a few sheep from the original property and kept them –

Table 7.6 Type of farming and the nature of other occupations

Type of farming	Farm-based enterprise	Work on other farms	Off-farm job
	per cent of holdings		
Dairying	26.6	17.3	14.0
Cattle and sheep	32.2	29.1	41.0
Arable and mixed	22.6	41.7	20.5
Horticulture	7.3	4.9	8.2
Other	11.3	7.0	16.3
All holdings	100.0 ***	100.0 ***	100.0 ***

(*Source*: 1984 farm survey, sample results)

there's no money in them, of course, but they add to the tranquility' (McQuin 1978:61).

The fact that dairying is more often associated with farm-based enterprises than with other types of non-farm activity could be explained in various ways. Imposition of dairy quotas has forced many milk producers to seek additional sources of income. An alternative enterprise on the farm or, better still, one managed by the farmer's wife, need not interfere with the farmer's continued management of the herd. Again, milk production is the predominant enterprise in some of the most popular holiday areas such as Devon and Cornwall, which would also help to account for the connection between dairy farming and farm-based enterprises.

One way in which farmers with other activities can simplify their farming operations is to choose less demanding enterprises like beef rather than milk production. Another is to carry fewer enterprises. In the Kent and East Sussex survey the average number of farm enterprises was 2.5 for part-time and 3.6 for full-time farms of similar size in the same parishes (Gasson 1967). More than half the part-time holdings studied by Ashton and Cracknell had no more than two enterprises, a quarter only one (Ashton and Cracknell 1961:492). Over half the New South Wales rural retreaters had two enterprises or less on their farms with an average of 2.6 per holding. More complex farming systems were followed by those who were interested in making an income from their farms and by those who were seeking self-sufficiency or lower living costs (McQuin 1978:73–5). In the pilot study the average was 1.9 enterprises per part-time holding but the number varied significantly depending on the importance of farming to the household economy. Class I part-time farms averaged 2.6 enterprises, Class IIa 1.8 and Class IIb only 1.5 enterprises. More than half the Class II part-time farms had only one enterprise.

LAND USE

From the information already gleaned on farming systems it is expected that part-time farmers as a whole will use land extensively with a high proportion of grassland and unproductive land and that these trends will be more pronounced, the less important farming is to the total income of the household. Data from the pilot study confirm these expectations (Table 7.7). Most of the farmers who took part allowed the researchers to have access to their 1981 June Returns. Analysis revealed that part-time farms as a whole had a smaller proportion of tillage but more grazing land (improved grass-land plus rough grazing), more woodland and more land taken up with roads, buildings and unproductive uses than full-time farms. A similar pattern emerges when Class I and Class II part-time farms are compared, Class II having relatively more grassland and land not farmed.

Table 7.7 Land use in part-time holdings by income class compared with all holdings in England and Wales in 1981

Type of use	Class I	Class IIa	Class IIb	All part time	England and Wales
	per cent of agricultural area				
Crops and fallow	49.7	26.5	37.3	43.9	47.5
Grass and rough grazing	47.5	69.5	54.2	51.8	49.5
Woodland and waste	2.8	4.0	8.5	4.3	3.0
Total area	100.0	100.0	100.0	100.0	100.0

(*Source*: pilot study, Ministry of Agriculture, Fisheries and Food 1982)

Further analysis showed that Class I part-time farmers as a group used less of their arable land for cereals and more for higher value, labour-intensive crops like roots and potatoes, fruit and vegetables. The proportion of tillage under cereals was 81 per cent on Class I farms, 92 per cent in Class IIb. Not all part-time farmers conformed to this pattern however. The pilot study identified a group of pensioners in Class IIb who were running mini-farms with a variety of enterprises and consequently making very intensive use of a small area. Another divergent group were Class I part-time farmers who also worked on other farms. Here the cropped area was generally large but most of it (90 per cent) was down to cereals. These farmers represent the very antithesis of hobby farmers. Work on the home farm would not be a form of recreation for them but highly competitive with the other job in terms of the farmer's time and energy. Having most of the arable under cereals suggests that these farmers are trying to rationalise and simplify their farming systems.

Class II part-time farmers not only put more of their land down to grass but also had a higher proportion of woodland and waste. There was three times as much non-agricultural land, relatively speaking, in Class IIb as in Class I. This would be partly an effect of farm size because the proportion of land taken up by the farmhouse and roads would be greater on a smaller holding. The non-agricultural land would not necessarily be idle. Where the farmer's main occupation was a farm-based enterprise, for instance, some 9 per cent of the holding area on average was taken up with woodland and other uses including perhaps caravan sites, nature trails and the like.

Dependence on another income source may also affect the way the land is maintained since occupiers who are less dependent on their farms financially may take less interest in them. This proposition was tested by Munton (1983:126–31) in his study of land use in London's Green Belt. He discovered that standards of land maintenance on full-time farms were no better or worse than the sample average. Highest standards of maintenance were recorded where farmers combined farming with off-farm income. Farmers who were heavily dependent on farm-based enterprises, although few in number, had by far and away the worst maintenance standards. Hobby farmers, defined as those acquiring 90 per cent or more of their income from off-farm sources, roughly equivalent to Class IIb in the present study, were associated with poorer maintenance standards than other Green Belt farmers. More than half the land on hobby farms was under-used or showed signs of being poorly maintained and a further 7 per cent was in a derelict or semi-derelict condition.

Munton discovered that those who kept horses in large numbers, corresponding perhaps with substantial reliance on farm-based enterprises in the present study, had below average standards of land maintenance. With a link having been established between the keeping of horses and run-down land, it is tempting to conclude that horse keeping damages the environment. Elsewhere attention has been drawn to the deterioration of the landscape in areas like London's Green Belt. Large numbers of pony paddocks contributed to this deterioration. Inadequate grassland management, unkept field boundaries, unsightly buildings used to shelter ponies and garishly coloured jumps all make for an untidy appearance (Jolliffe 1977:38).

As Munton has pointed out, however, the direction of causality might be the other way. It is possible that some horse grazing is conducted on poorly reclaimed mineral land not capable of supporting the grazing needs of more intensive livestock enterprises. In other words, horse grazing may be as much a symptom as a cause of poor land maintenance and a response to insecurity and uncertainty over the land's future use.

MEASURES OF PERFORMANCE

The evidence presented so far suggests that farmers who are less dependent on farming for their livelihood use their land less intensively than the rest. The evidence has been mainly descriptive and circumstantial; no account has been taken of the size of individual enterprises, for instance. Using the agricultural census information which was available in the pilot study it was possible to measure intensity of land use more objectively and quantify differences between income classes.

Stocking density

The only measure of land-use intensity which varied in the expected direction with income class was stocking density. The measure used here was standard labour requirements for all grazing livestock (dairy cows, other cattle and sheep) per hectare of grazing land (improved grassland plus rough grazing). Over the sample as a whole, stocking density averaged 4.5 grazing livestock smd per ha but it ranged from 6.3 smd/ha on Class I holdings through 4.0 smd/ha in Class IIa to 3.0 smd/ha in Class IIb. Thus farmers relying more heavily on farm incomes appear to make more intensive use of grassland. This is in line with the OECD's conclusion that the stocking rate on grassland is lower on part-time than on full-time farms. In Ireland, too, full-time farmers kept significantly more livestock units per hectare than full-timers. Further investigation revealed, however, that this was mainly due to full-time farmers' greater concentration in milk production where stocking density was usually higher. With the type of farming controlled, full-time farmers did not achieve significantly higher stocking rates than part-timers (Higgins 1983:79–80).

Other measures of land-use intensity

No other measure of land-use intensity showed the expected relationship with income class. One such measure was the standard labour requirement per hectare, an indicator of the intensity of the whole farming system. Standard labour requirements are a proxy for output and so give a rough guide to the level of production expected. This measure can be viewed as a reflection of the farmer's *intentions* towards the farm business; whether these intentions are realised will depend on many intervening factors such as the standard of management and the weather.

Table 7.8 Intensity of land use on part-time farms by main income source with size of holding controlled

Size of holding in smd	Main living farms		Supplementary income farms	
	smd/ha	N	smd/ha	N
Under 100	2.7	43	3.3	163
100 to 249	5.6	46	7.7	55
250 and over	8.2	45	14.7	63

(*Source*: pilot study)

Over the pilot study sample as a whole, farming intensity averaged 6.6 smd/ha with a strong positive association between intensity and size of farm business. There was no significant difference between Class I and Class II over the whole sample. When size of holding was controlled a clear link appeared but it was not in the expected direction. For each holding size group, supplementary income (Class II) farmers made *more* intensive use of land than main living farmers (Table 7.8). It seems likely that a number of influences are at work here, resulting in a very complex pattern. On one hand, where farming is the main occupation and source of income the farmer is likely to choose more labour-intensive enterprises and devote more time to the business than where farming is subsidiary. Working against this, where farming is the main activity holdings are usually larger, which means that inputs and outputs are spread more thinly. In addition some of the Class II occupiers who farm on a very small scale as a hobby or to give them an interest in retirement deliberately choose labour-demanding enterprises and spend longer over farm work than is economically justified. This helps to push up the intensity of land use in Class II.

There is little direct evidence that full-time farms perform any better than part-time ones, once farm size and enterprise mix have been allowed for. In the pilot study, for example, there were no systematic differences between the income classes in actual labour inputs per hectare with size controlled. Higgins found no significant difference between full-time and part-time farms in terms of gross margin or gross output per hectare when type of farming was controlled. The Kent and East Sussex survey produced no evidence of differences in standard output per acre between part-time and full-time farms. Although rather more part-time than full-time farms operated at very low levels of intensity there were some highly intensive part-time farms (Gasson 1966). Reviewing the Canadian literature Bollman (1982) came to the conclusion that part-time farming does not imply inefficient land use or inefficient food production. For Britain the case is not proven. More research is needed to disentangle the effects of scale of operations, enterprise mix, level of inputs and yields in part-time and full-time farms.

Efficiency of labour use

It is widely believed that part-time farming is negatively associated with efficient use of capital and land resources but positively associated with efficient use of labour resources (see, for example, Martens 1980; Cavazzani and Fuller 1982; Arkleton Trust 1985: 15–16). The Productivity Steering Group of the Agriculture EDC identified the farmer's age and having labour surplus to requirements as the two factors most closely related to low performance on British farms. Small family farms in particular were singled out as having a high proportion of labour surplus to requirements (Agriculture EDC 1973). Britton and Hill (1975:132–6) concluded, too, that underemployment of the farmer and wife's labour was one of the main causes of low productivity on small farms. If some of this surplus can be absorbed by another activity, labour productivity on the farm should improve. Moss has argued that labour efficiency on part-time small-scale beef and sheep farms in Northern Ireland is better than commonly supposed because off-farm working reduces the average labour input on the farm. Where the farmer works full time, structural unemployment is clearly a problem (Moss 1980:52).

The Kent and East Sussex study tried to compare the efficiency of labour use on 74 part-time and 73 full-time farms (Gasson 1966). The total amount of labour available on each holding, expressed in man-days per annum, was compared with the theoretical labour requirement which was obtained by applying labour standards to acres of crops and numbers of livestock on the holding. Over the whole sample it was calculated that some 119 000 smd working days were available while an estimated 139 000 smd were required. (Some of the difference was due to the hiring of agricultural contractors for which no allowance was made in the calculation.) Overall the ratio of days available to days required was 86 per cent. This was the 'labour efficiency index', lower values indicating greater efficiency.

A labour-efficiency index of 89 for all part-time farms in the sample and 84 for full-time farms means that part-time farms as a whole made less efficient use of the available labour than full-time. The difference was surprisingly small and there was a wide variation within each group, some farms being highly mechanised so that a single man could accomplish a large amount of work and others employing more men than were strictly necessary in order to keep on top of the work. More part-time farms (23 per cent) than full-time (11 per cent) were highly inefficient in the sense that they were using more than twice the amount of labour theoretically required but equal numbers were highly efficient, using less than three-quarters of the theoretical requirement.

Further analysis showed that labour efficiency was influenced more by the type of farming than by full-time or part-time working. The study areas were divided into predominantly livestock and predominantly arable. Livestock areas seemed to make more efficient use of labour on average with a labour-efficiency index of 78 compared with 94 for arable areas. This may reflect the difficulties of keeping workers usefully employed on arable farms during the winter months. On livestock farms labour requirements are more evenly distributed throughout the year. Besides this many of the smaller livestock farms in the sample used agricultural contractors for haymaking and harvesting. While full-time farmers made more efficient use of labour than part timers in the arable districts, the reverse was true in the livestock areas as Table 7.9 shows.

A similar exercise was attempted for the part-time holdings in the pilot study, the actual number of man days devoted to farm work in 1979/80 being compared with the standard labour requirement for each holding. Labour standards are periodically revised downwards

Table 7.9 Labour efficiency on full-time and part-time farms by type of farming area

Type of farming area	Part-time	Full-time	All farms
	Labour-efficiency index		
Arable	98	90	94
Livestock	77	79	78
All types	89	84	86

(*Source*: Kent and East Sussex survey)

to reflect more economical use of manpower in agriculture over time. On large farms in particular, use of large tractors, higher rates of working, wide implements and high-capacity equipment in fields of adequate size have led to remarkable economies in labour use in the last twenty years. The majority of part-time holdings are below the minimum size for which labour standards are calculated which helps to explain why labour usage over the pilot sample as a whole was considerably above the recommended level. The average part-time holding used 383 man days in 1979/80 while its average labour requirement was 207 smd, giving an overall labour-efficiency index of 185. In other words part-time farms appear to use nearly twice as much labour as theoretically required.

Table 7.10 confirms that this is largely due to their small size. Part-time holdings over 500 smd use little more than the theoretical labour requirement whilst those below 250 smd use more than twice as much and holdings below 50 smd use between seven and eight times the theoretical norm.

Table 7.10 Labour efficiency on part-time farms by size of holding

Size of holding in smd	Mean labour use in days/holding	Mean labour requirement in smd/holding	Labour efficiency index
Under 50	159	21	760
50 to 99	219	73	300
100 to 249	379	158	240
250 to 499	477	340	140
500 and over	1 307	1 197	109
All holdings	383	207	185

(*Source*: pilot study)

Although part-time farms as a whole do not make very efficient use of labour on the evidence of the pilot study, efficiency is higher where farming is not the farmer's main occupation (Table 7.11). This finding is the more surprising in view of the fact that holdings where farming is not the main activity tend to be smaller and therefore inherently less efficient in labour terms than where farming is the major activity. The relationship is clarified in Table 7.12 where size of holding is controlled. Within each size band, Class II holdings use labour more efficiently than Class I. The gap narrows as farm size increases, indicating that the most severe problems of under employment of farmer and family labour occur on the smallest holdings where there are no adequate alternatives to farming.

Table 7.11 Efficiency of labour use on part-time farms by farmer's main activity

Main activity	Mean labour use in days/holding	Mean labour requirement in smd/holding	Labour-efficiency index
Farming	507	249	204
Not farming	291	180	162
All holdings	383	207	185

(*Source*: pilot study)

Table 7.12 Efficiency of labour use on part-time farms by income class with size of holding controlled

	Class I	Class II
Size of holding in smd	Labour-efficiency index	
Under 100	620	360
100 to 249	260	230
250 and over	140	120

(*Source*: pilot study)

FARMING CHANGE

Farm investment

Following the general tenor of the argument put forward so far, levels of capital investment ought to be lower on part-time than full-time farms and lower on supplementary income than on main-living farms. Rearing cattle or sheep requires less investment in specialised buildings and fixed equipment than production of milk, pigs or eggs. Against this must be set the argument that investment on full-time and larger Class I part-time farms may be 'diluted' by being spread over a larger area.

The OECD study recognised that the heterogeneous nature of part-time farmers would be likely to give rise to many forms of investment behaviour. Off-farm work may be undertaken in order to pay off debts and stock and equip the farm so that full-time farming will be possible at some later date. Off-farm income may enable the farmer to farm as he would like to rather than as he could afford to do on farm income alone. Part-time farms may need to carry excess machinery capacity to ensure that work can be done in the limited time available. Some part-time farmers run 'model' farms with excess machinery investment and with buildings kept in a far better state of repair than is strictly necessary for their agricultural function. In all these examples investment in the part-time farm would tend to be higher than on a comparable full-time farm operated for profit. On the other hand some part-time farmers regard their non-viable holdings as a place to live in the country rather than a small business. Here investment in farm machinery and buildings is frequently below what would be expected on full-time farms although investment in the farmhouse may be above average (OECD 1978:27–9).

In their study of rural industrial development in the communities of Scarriff and Tubbercurry in western Ireland Lucey and Kaldor (1969:178–9) found that 40 to 50 per cent of farm operators had increased the value of their farm output since obtaining employment in industry as a consequence of having more cash to invest in the farm. Similarly in New South Wales other income was used to finance farm improvements. Under 20 per cent of McQuin's rural retreaters had paid for farm improvements out of farm income alone and under 20 per cent planned to finance future investments by this means (McQuin 1978:87–8).

The farm surveys sought information on capital improvements made on the holding within the preceding five years. Respondents in the 1984 survey were asked about major investment in the fixed capital of the farm since the summer of 1979. The question was confined to improvements in the fixed or landlord's capital including farm buildings, roads and drainage. Improvements to the farmhouse and additions to working capital such as livestock and machinery were not considered. It was left to respondents to decide what constituted a 'major' improvement in the context of their particular farm business, the pilot study having demonstrated that one farmer's major improvement was another's minor repair. Amounts invested turned out to be quite modest by the standards of modern agriculture. More than half the investors in the pilot study had spent less than £5000 on the holding in the preceding five years and only one in six had exceeded £20 000. Net of grant, 90 per cent of projects totalled less than £20 000.

An estimated 27 000 part-time farms or 52 per cent of the total had made some significant capital improvement in the five years to 1984. The figure for the pilot study was 41 per cent, a difference due perhaps to the way the samples were drawn or a more favourable climate for investment in the later period. Both the pilot and main surveys found a strong positive association between farm size and the likelihood of an improvement being made.

In England and Wales there was no control group of full-time farmers to suggest a 'normal' rate of farm improvements but in Galway the proportion of part-time farmers making farm improvements (47 per cent) was below the average for full-time farms (61 per cent) (Cawley 1983:69–70). In a marginal farming area of central Italy the reverse was true with the value of agrarian capital, land capital, machinery and land improvements all greater on part-time than on full-time farms (Cavazzani 1976). The farm survey revealed a highly significant relationship between dependence on farm income and propensity to invest with 63 per cent of holdings in Class I, 49 per cent in Class IIa and 57 per cent in Class IIb reporting capital improvements having been made in the previous five years. It was surprising to find such a strong tendency to invest in holdings in Class IIb where dependence on farm income is weakest. The reason may be the importance which some Class IIb farmers attach to safeguarding and improving the capital value of the holding.

Further investigation showed that occupiers of larger and Class I part-time farms had invested relatively more in farm buildings and fixed equipment such as grain bins, milking parlours and water supplies while those on the smaller and Class II holdings spent relatively more on improving the land by drainage, fencing, liming and reclamation. The pilot study produced a similar result and in Galway, too, full-time farmers were found to have put a higher proportion of their investment into farm buildings while part timers veered more towards land reclamation (Cawley 1983:69–71). This may be a result of government policy, at least in the British case. According to the OECD,

> ... it is recognised by the United Kingdom Government that some aspects of investment on farms that are not potentially full-time viable holdings (even though the farmer may spend all his working time on the farm) should be discouraged. Government grants have, for several years, not been paid on investments in buildings or similar projects on such holdings. Grants are, however, paid for work, such as drainage, which would continue to be of value even if the holding were part of a larger unit (OECD 1978:29).

Most farm capital grants are now paid under the Agricultural Improvement Regulations which came into force in October 1985. To be eligible a business must provide at least 1100 man hours (nearly 140 man days) of work per year and show, by means of an improvement plan, that the proposed investment will bring about a lasting and substantial improvement to the business and raise income per labour unit. As well as possessing adequate agricultural skill and competence, applicants must spend at least half their working time in the agricultural business and derive at least half their income from it. Similar conditions of eligibility are attached to the suckler-cow subsidy. These restrictions effectively exclude the Class II part-time farmer from receiving capital grants or the beef-cow subsidy. Conditions attached to previous grant schemes had much the same effect.

The farm survey confirmed that obtaining grant aid for farm improvements was closely linked with the size of the holding and the level of dependence on farm income. As Table 7.13 shows, only half the Class IIb part-time farmers making substantial farm improvements in the period 1979 to 1984 had received grant aid for any project as compared with 79 per cent of investors in Class I. The indications were that farmers who had had grant applications turned down were most likely to come from the smallest holdings and to belong to Class IIa although these relationships were not significant. The opposite situation seems to hold on small beef and sheep farms in Northern Ireland where more part-time than full-time farmers had received grants in the period 1968 to 1978 (Moss 1980:48–9).

Table 7.13 Grant aid for farm improvements on part-time farms by size of holding and income class

Size band	Per cent of improvements grant aided	Income class	Per cent of improvements grant aided
1	35.5	I	78.5
2	60.0	IIa	58.4
3	71.5	IIb	50.0
4	85.6		
	***		***

(*Source*: 1984 farm survey, sample results)

Not all farmers take the trouble to apply for grants on farm improvements. A handful of respondents in the pilot study said that they objected to government handouts in principle but more believed that they would not be eligible or were disinclined to fill in the necessary forms. High standards of work required before a project could be approved for a grant acted as a disincentive to some. These farmers preferred to put up buildings and make improvements with their own labour, using whatever materials came to hand. The final result might not meet the Ministry's rigid specifications but it would serve its purpose. It became obvious from conversations with part-time farmers that weekend building projects can provide a form of recreation. Some people gain great satisfaction from improvising, overcoming the problems and seeing improvements they have made with their own hands.

Changes in the area of holdings

Respondents in the farm surveys were questioned about gains and losses of land over the preceding five years. From both studies it emerged that gains had outnumbered losses and that more gains than losses had exceeded 10 ha, so the net effect was one of farm enlargement. It is logically impossible for farms in the aggregate to expand without new land being created but it should be remembered that any sample of farms drawn at a given time is a sample of survivors. Those who had given up farming and surrendered their land to other farms could not have appeared in the surveys.

It is widely held that the presence of substantial numbers of part-time farmers in an area hampers structural reform which in a European context usually means the enlargement of existing full-time farms. Progress towards farm enlargement is slow in any case because land ownership acts as a brake but the presence of part-time farmers who are reluctant to leave their farms retards it still further. The ability of some wealthy part-time farmers to outbid full-timers in competition for land may be bitterly resented (Craps 1977:18; Bergmann and Laurent 1977:10).

Part-time farmers in the Kent and East Sussex survey were significantly less likely than full-timers to have made any change in the area of the holding since first acquiring it. More than a third of full-time but only a quarter of part-time farmers had added to their holdings during their occupancy. While it is plausible to argue that full-time farmers have more incentive to expand the business it should also be borne in mind that full-time farmers had spent longer on their present holdings on average, giving them more opportunity to acquire extra land.

Following the same trend, the farm survey indicated that 29 per cent of all part-time farmers had made some change in the size of their holdings in the previous five years while the figure for the pilot study was 25 per cent. These were assumed to be low rates of land mobility since considerably higher rates were recorded for random samples of farms in Somerset and Northern Ireland by Edwards (1980, 1982). There was also a highly significant and positive association between holding size and acreage gains. Table 7.14 shows, as might be expected, that Class I part-time holdings were significantly more likely than those in Class II to have gained land in the previous five years and to have gained 10 ha or more; there was no systematic variation in respect of losses.

Table 7.14 Increases in area of part-time holdings by income class

Change in area	Class I	Class IIa	Class IIb
	per cent of holdings		
No change	69.8	83.8	85.3
Gain of less than 10 ha	11.2	8.4	8.0
Gain of 10 ha or more	19.0	7.8	6.7
All holdings	100.0	100.0	100.0 ***

(*Source*: 1984 farm survey, sample results)

Although only a minority of the part-time farmers interviewed had made any permanent or long-term change in the area of their holdings in the preceding five years, usually by buying or selling land, this does not mean that there was no scope for adjusting the area farmed to changing family needs. Earlier in this chapter it was pointed out that a great deal of flexibility was achieved by means of grazing tenancies and other seasonal or short-term and informal arrangements. These transfers had the great advantage of being reversible.

Changes in farm enterprises

Respondents were asked if there had been any major changes in farm enterprises in the previous five years. Again it was left to them to decide what constituted a 'major' change in relation to their own farm business. From the replies it was estimated that 39 per cent of all part-time farms in England and Wales had undergone some major reorganisation in the period 1979 to 1984, the corresponding figure for the pilot study being 40 per cent. Both surveys found that larger farms were significantly more likely than smaller ones to have made some change in the farming system. Class I part-time farms were twice as likely as those in Class IIb to have expanded an existing enterprise whilst starting a new one, giving up or contracting an enterprise or giving up land were all more characteristic of Class IIb.

Farmers in the pilot study were asked whether they had firm plans to make any major changes in the way the farm was run in the next two years. Firm plans were those which the farmer had a reasonable expectation of fulfilling, as opposed to mere wishful thinking. Only 27 per cent of the part-time farmers had any major changes planned, the remaining 73 per cent apparently feeling satisfied with the present state of affairs or perceiving some obstacle to change. The same proportion of rural retreaters in New South Wales intended to continue the present farming enterprise unaltered because they were content with the present situation, disinclined to risk more capital or invest more labour in the property or prevented by climatic, physical or other constraints (McQuin 1978:88). The pilot study discovered that 20 per cent of main living but 30 per cent of supplementary income farmers had some change planned, a difference which was statistically significant but not in the expected direction. A possible explanation might be that an external source of income is needed to finance change and that the risk associated with a major change is more acceptable if the family can rely on another, main source of income.

CONCLUSIONS

This chapter has brought together information from a number of sources to build up a picture of the typical part-time farm. It has revealed that compared with full-time farms, those run on a part-time basis are predominantly small and owner-occupied, the presumption being that some part-time farmers are more interested in owning land than farming it. Part-time farms tend to be operated on simple lines with few enterprises and with an emphasis on beef, sheep and cereals rather than on dairy cows and the more labour-intensive crops. The same kind of pattern emerges when main living and supplementary income part-time farms are compared; that is to say Class II holdings tend to be smaller than Class I with more land owned, they carry fewer and less labour-intensive enterprises with less arable and more grassland, woodland and waste and the land may not be so well maintained.

From this it might be expected that part-time farms in general and supplementary income farms in particular would make less productive use of their land than full-time and main-living farms. While the evidence on stocking density supports this proposition it is difficult to find other conclusive proof. For one thing, whole farm measures of inputs or outputs per hectare cannot usually distinguish performance in yield terms from the effects of enterprise mix. For another, although farmers who are less dependent on farm incomes tend to choose less intensive systems they operate them on smaller areas so the level of inputs per unit area may not be lower and may even be higher than on full-time and main-living farms. More detailed research using carefully designed comparisons would be necessary before firmer conclusions could be drawn.

The findings on efficiency of labour use suggest that although part-time farming may be associated with a rather wasteful use of labour compared with what is achieved on the average full-time farm, this is largely an effect of farm size. Existence of another, main occupation leads to more efficient use of labour on the small part-time farm. This is true despite the fact that where farming is not pursued seriously for a living, certain practices may be introduced for their conservation, aesthetic or recreational value and such practices are likely to be very labour-intensive; ploughing with horses is a good example.

Holdings where farming is combined with some other activity are not, as a rule, in the vanguard of change. According to the latest survey only just over half of all part-time farms had experienced any major capital improvement, under 40 per cent a major change in the system of farming and under 30 per cent any change in holding area in the period 1979 to 1984. Farming change is more characteristic of the larger, main-living type of part-time farm which tends to invest more heavily in permanent structures and installations, to purchase rather than sell land and to expand rather than give up an enterprise. Where change has occurred on smaller and supplementary income farms, acreage gains are usually small, investment more often of the land-improving type and enterprises contracted or given up rather than expanded. These data do not support the suggestion that part-time farming is pursued primarily as a means of accumulating capital so that full-time farming may be possible. A more likely explanation is that having another job interferes with the growth and development of the farm business. There are several reasons why this might be so.

One obstacle to growth on the part-time farm is the way government grant schemes are administered. The bias in grant aid towards the larger, full-time or Class I part-time farm was very apparent in both the pilot and main surveys. This has probably served to discourage investment on smaller part-time farms and possibly undermined their viability and chances of survival.

Secondly, many farmers with other occupations simply do not have the time to devote to developing the farm business which entails keeping abreast of technical progress, seeking advice, attending conferences, demonstrations, training courses, discussion groups and so on. Many would not be interested in change if it meant increasing an already heavy workload or adding to the complexity of management. The rapid growth in technical sophistication in modern farming seems bound to widen the gap between progressive professional farmers and those for whom farming is only a sideline.

Thirdly, the trend towards farm enlargement and modernisation is driven by rising costs and falling real prices for farm products. Part-time farmers are cushioned to some extent from the cost-price squeeze by their other source of income. They are not under the same pressure as full-time farmers to increase output or to strive for ever higher efficiency. They may be more interested in holding land as an investment and for its amenity value than in making an income from it. The question of what part-time farmers want out of farming will be considered in more detail in Chapter 9. Meanwhile Chapter 8 explores the dynamics of part-time farming.

The dynamics of part-time farming

TRENDS IN PART-TIME FARMING

So far part-time farming has been treated as if it were a static phenomenon. Information gathered in surveys has been related to a point in time, usually the date of the survey or the preceding twelve-month period. In reality the part-time farming population is in a constant state of flux with some families leaving agriculture or moving on to full-time farming and others entering the population each year. Information about the rate of change and the direction of underlying trends would be valuable for the policy maker. Any net increase or decrease in the number of farm families with other gainful activities could have far-reaching implications for income support in the agricultural sector, as Chapter 6 has suggested. In view of the diversity of the part-time farming population it makes good sense to disaggregate the whole into more homogeneous sub-groups. In Chapter 7 a clear distinction was beginning to emerge between Class I or main living and Class II or supplementary income farms, in terms of farm size and type and the occupier's propensity to develop the business. In countries where statistics have been collected for several years, the general trend is for Class II part-time farms to increase relative to Class I and full-time farms (OECD 1978:41). Any indications of changes in the relative importance of Class I and Class II part-time farms in Britain would be highly relevant to an assessment of trends in farm structure.

Trends in part-time farming are difficult to pin down. Up to now few governments have felt the subject sufficiently important to mount large-scale surveys at regular intervals while individual researchers or institutions have not usually had the resources to do so. This means that trends can only be inferred from census and survey data which were collected for other purposes. Definitions of part-time farming will not necessarily be the most suitable for the task nor consistent from one survey or census to the next.

For England and Wales a crude indication of trends can be obtained by comparing results of the 1983 LII and subsequent 1984 farm survey with those of the National Farm Survey of 1941/3 (Ministry of Agriculture and Fisheries 1946). On that occasion all agricultural holdings of 5 acres (2 ha) and above were classified by 'economic type of occupier' using a scheme developed by Thomas and Elms (1938) in their survey of Buckinghamshire farms. Thomas and Elms' 'part-time occupiers' who rely mainly on farming for their income but draw additional income from other sources correspond to the present Class I. 'Spare-time occupiers' who farm as a source of income but have some other main employment, are equivalent to Class IIa while their 'hobby and other' category where land is occupied for convenience or pleasure rather than for profit, can be equated with Class IIb. Allowance needs to be made for differences in definition and coverage between the two surveys; the National Farm Survey did not take account of spouses' activities, for example. Nevertheless the thinking behind the two classification schemes is sufficiently similar to justify the comparison.

The total number of holdings to which the 1983 LII referred was little more than half the number in the National Farm Survey due mainly to small holdings being excluded from the agricultural census, absorbed by larger farms or going out of agricultural use. This should have had the effect of removing many part-time units, yet the proportion of part-time farms in the total actually rose a little, from 26 per cent in 1941/3 to 31 per cent in 1983. The most likely explanation is that part-time farming has encroached on what were formerly full-time farms.

According to the last column in Table 8.1 it is the growth in Class IIb farms which is mainly responsible for the increase in part-time farming. Numbers of full-time and Class I part-time farms have been almost halved and Class IIa reduced by more than a third while numbers in Class IIb actually rose by nearly one-fifth. In view of the fact that holdings in the 1984 farm survey were designated Class IIa or IIb on the strength of a single year's reported farm income results, it would be unwise to read too much into these figures. A more cautious conclusion would be that numbers of supplementary income farms, those represented by spare-time and hobby farms in 1941/3 and by Class II in 1983/4, have fallen by less than 20 per cent whilst full-

Table 8.1 Classification of agricultural holdings in England and Wales according to main source of income, 1941/3 and 1983/4

Economic type 1941/3	Numbers 000s	Per cent	Income class 1983/4	Numbers 000s	Per cent	Percentage change
Full-time	216	74.3	Full-time	119	69.3	−45
Part-time	33	11.2	Class I	18	10.6	−44
Spare-time	28	9.8	Class IIa	18	10.5	−37
Hobby, other	14	4.7	Class IIb	16	9.5	+18
All holdings	291	100.0		170	100.0	−41

(*Sources*: Ministry of Agriculture and Fisheries 1946, 1983 Labour Input Inquiry, 1984 farm survey, raised results)

time and main income part-time farms have decreased by over 40 per cent. This is in line with the trend in other countries for Class II part-time farms to increase relative to Class I and full-time farms.

THE VALUE OF A LIFE-HISTORY APPROACH

Comparing cross sections of the farm population at different dates, as in Table 8.1, gives a broad picture of structural change without revealing the underlying causes. Small net changes often conceal gross changes which are many times larger. In the United States, for instance, Hathaway and Perkins (1968:187) found that 19 per cent of farmers who reported income from off-farm employment in one year were employed exclusively in non-farm jobs in the following year. The *net* reduction in numbers of farmers was, however, very much smaller. A longitudinal study, following the fortunes of a given set of farms or families through time, is capable of yielding far more information on factors contributing to farm structural change. But longitudinal studies are bound to be time-consuming and therefore expensive. The usual compromise is to collect information at one point in time but to include questions relating to an earlier period. The drawback of this approach is that it becomes a study of survivors; those who have dropped out of the population for any reason cannot be sampled.

Information about the past as well as the present occupational status of farm occupiers would find a number of applications. It would, for example, be helpful for those whose job it is to provide advice and training in agriculture. The way a farmer approaches his business, the farming system he favours, the kinds of decisions he makes and therefore the information he needs will be shaped to some degree by his background and previous experience. Knowledge of the farmer's future plans would also be relevant since his present actions help to determine and in a sense are also determined by what he hopes to achieve eventually. Among today's population of part-time farmers there could well be more demand for courses in basic agriculture for novice farmers than for the kind of advice and training which would help established farmers to diversify into other enterprises. At the present time many agricultural advisers seem willing to cater for the latter need while denying any responsibility towards the former.

Attitudes of agricultural advisers towards part-time farming seem to reflect a widely held belief in the superiority of full-time farming. With full-time farming regarded as the norm, part-time farming is seen as inherently unstable and therefore undesirable. While it is recognised that members of farm families may seek outside employment at certain stages in the family cycle, for example to build up capital in the early phase, it is usually assumed that this will be a temporary arrangement. Part-time farming has frequently been described as a transitional stage for families on the way into, or more likely out of, full-time commercial agriculture. One familiar stereotype is the farmer from a non-farming background, a newcomer who aspires to farm full time but is unwilling to relinquish off-farm employment until the farm business is on a secure financial footing. Another is the family using part-time farming as a stepping stone on the way out of agriculture, a means of trying out other jobs, gaining work experience, assimilating different values, becoming accustomed to a new lifestyle, before making the final break with farming.

With full-time commercial farming the goal of agricultural policy, it has seemed appropriate to encourage part-time farmers either to build up their businesses into viable full-time units or, where this is not feasible, to quit farming altogether and allow their land to be used to enlarge other units. This was the thrust of the package of three EC farm structural directives put forward in 1972. Pursuing a long-term goal of increasing agricultural productivity and ensuring a fair standard of living for those engaged in agriculture, the directives aimed to modernise and enlarge viable farms, to encourage the cessation of farming and the amalgamation of uneconomic units and to provide socio-economic guidance and assistance in acquiring new skills for those whose future in agriculture was in some doubt.

If part-time farming were merely a transitional phase, a means of mopping up surplus labour generated in the process of farm structural change, it should now be on the decline in all the developed countries whereas it is generally increasing (Martens 1980). Recognition that part-time farming could be a stable and legitimate status in its own right, an end in itself rather than a means to an end, seems to have stemmed from research carried out in Canada during the 1970s. More than half the part-time farmers interviewed in four separate regions of Ontario were identified as 'persistent part-time farmers'. They had been farming on the same basis for a minimum of six years which was judged time enough, under the prevailing economic conditions, for them to have switched to full-time farming or left agriculture altogether if that had been their intention (Galloway 1975). Further analysis suggested that persistent part-time farmers were a distinct group differing in a number of respects from those in the process of entering or leaving full-time agriculture (Fuller 1976:49).

THEORETICAL AND EMPIRICAL APPROACHES

If the part-time farming population includes not only families in a state of transition and those whose mobility has been blocked but also some who have consciously chosen to farm part-time and are content to continue doing so, a fresh policy approach may be called for. A prerequisite of any such approach would be information on the past histories and future intentions of existing farmers and their families. Several attempts have been made to classify farmers according to the way their careers have developed. Fuguitt (1961) proposed a typology based on the part-time farmer's past, present and future commitment to the farm and non-farm occupations which he tested with a sample of part-time farmers in Wisconsin. The Wye College workshop (Centre for European Agricultural Studies 1977) endorsed the value of such an approach for policy purposes and suggested that the conceptual framework should be extended to include whole families. A twenty-seven cell matrix was devised by combining three occupational statuses (full-time farming, part-time farming and not farming) with three time periods (past, present and future). Although this ambitious scheme was never put to the test, Mage (1976) introduced a number of 'career' variables into his empirical analysis of Ontario part-time farmers including years spent as a part-time farmer, operator's background, future plans and son's intentions to farm. Combining theory with pragmatism Kada (1980) identified four types of part-time farmer in Wisconsin based on the past and present activities of the farmer and family:

(a) transitional, where the farm enterprise was in operation before any member of the family took up an off-farm job;
(b) persistent, where the present operator entered agriculture as a

part-time farmer and continued combining farming with another job;

(c) U-turn, where the present operator had a farming background before starting an urban occupation and at a later date the family moved back to farming without relinquishing off-farm employment;

(d) entrant, where the family took up farming although no member had any background in farming.

The value of a life-cycle approach, amply demonstrated by Kada's work, provided new insights in the pilot study. This approach does, however, involve a detailed and usually lengthy discussion of the respondent's family history. In view of the limited time available for each farm interview in the main survey it was not possible to investigate the work history of each household member. Rather than abandon the approach altogether, it was decided that the enquiry would focus on a few critical points in the farmer's career; whether he had begun his working life on the land, when and how the present holding was acquired, whether a successor was expected and so on. With this information it was not possible to classify the part-time farming families or even farmers according to their past, present and future occupational states. Even so, the variables which were selected proved to be highly correlated with many other aspects of part-time farming, adding significantly to an understanding of the current situation.

DEVELOPMENT OF THE FARMER'S CAREER

Farming or farm work had been the first major occupation after completing full-time education and National Service for an estimated 28 815 occupiers of part-time holdings in England and Wales, or 55 per cent. Other studies have also suggested that roughly half of all part-time farmers began their careers in agriculture, with figures of 48 per cent in the pilot study and 52 per cent for 'Grey Zone' occupiers in Scotland (Dunn 1969). By way of comparison, 86 per cent of full-time farmers in England and Wales had entered agriculture straight from school (Agriculture EDC 1972).

Whilst many young men intending to become farmers begin their working lives on the family holding, others deliberately seek more varied experience before settling down to farm. The survey therefore tried to establish if farming had at any time been the farmer's main occupation. Here the estimate was 31 750 farmers or 61 per cent. Exactly half the part-time farmers claimed that farming was their main occupation at the time of the survey, suggesting some drift away from farming for the group as a whole. A total of 31 808 occupiers (61 per cent) had intended farming to become the main occupation when they took over the present holding. Most had achieved this ambition by the time of the survey but some never would. This still leaves nearly 40 per cent of all part-time farmers who are either satisfied with the present situation or see no prospect of changing it. The persistent part-time farmer seems to be well represented in England and Wales today.

The work history of the farmer's spouse was explored in the pilot but not the main survey. The most important discovery was that spouses were far less likely than farmers to have made farming their main activity at any stage. Only 14 per cent of spouses but 48 per cent of farmers had started their working lives on the land. Farming had at some time been the main activity for 65 per cent of farmers in the pilot study but for only 33 per cent of their spouses.

The farmer's past experience was closely linked with farm size, the proportion who began their careers in agriculture rising from 44 per cent in band 1 to 71 per cent in band 4. In the Scottish studies, too, the proportion of occupiers for whom farming came first chronologically increased with farm size (Dunn 1969; Wagstaff 1970). There was also a link with the nature of the other activity. Farmers involved with farm-based enterprises and work on other farms tended to be those whose careers had begun on the land; typically these were ex-full-time farmers diversifying into other activities. Those whose other job was off-farm employment or a home business were more likely to have come into agriculture subsequently or had always combined farming with another, major activity.

The farmer's past experience and future plans proved to be highly correlated with the family's dependence on farm income at the present time. More than 80 per cent of the farmers in Class I had begun their working lives on the land and more than 90 per cent had at some time farmed as the main occupation and had expected farming to be the main occupation when they took over the present holding. Corresponding figures were 53 per cent for Class IIa and under 50 per cent for members of Class IIb (Table 8.2).

Combining the farmer's first and present main occupation gives the basis for a new typology. An estimated 35 per cent of all occupiers of part-time farms have always regarded farming as their main if not sole occupation. A further 30 per cent are in the opposite position, farming never having been the main occupation. The rest are in a state of transition; 20 per cent are 'leavers' for whom farming was originally but is no longer the main job and 15 per cent are 'entrants', making farming their main occupation now although it was not so originally. This breakdown is closely related to holding size. Those for whom farming has always been the main activity are mostly to be found in bands 2 to 4 and those for whom it has never been the main occupation are concentrated in band 1. The proportion classified as

Table 8.2 Development of farmer's career by income class

Income class	Farming was the farmer's main activity:		
	on leaving school	at some stage	intended when farm acquired
	per cent of farmers		
I	80.4	95.0	91.7
IIa	53.4	53.0	53.0
IIb	35.6	42.4	48.5
	***	***	***

(*Source*: 1984 farm survey, sample results)

leavers decreases rapidly with increasing farm size. Entrants are more evenly spread across all size groups although rather more common in bands 3 and 4 than in 1 or 2 (Table 8.3).

The tendency for farmers to have begun their careers in agriculture is noticeably stronger down the eastern side of England and in the more rural areas than elsewhere. More than 60 per cent of occupiers of part-time holdings in East Anglia, the East Midlands, Yorkshire/Humberside and the north region had started working on the land when they left school while little more than 40 per cent in the most urban areas, the north-west and south-east of England, had done so. In Figure 8.1 East Anglia and the north region stand out as having the highest proportion of farmers always putting farming first while the south-east has an exceptionally large number with farming never the main activity. Leavers are well represented in Yorkshire/Humberside, eastern England and Wales while entrants seem

Table 8.3 Development of farmer's career by size of holding

Size band	Always	Leaver	Entrant	Never	All farmers
	per cent of farmers				
1	16.5	27.2	13.8	42.5	100.0
2	50.2	14.8	13.5	21.5	100.0
3	55.8	12.5	18.0	13.7	100.0
4	65.3	5.7	17.9	11.1	100.0
All farmers	35.1	19.9	15.3	29.8	100.0 ***
Numbers	18 376 *a*	10 440 *b*	7 953 *b*	15 576 *b*	52 344

(*Source*: 1984 farm survey, raised results)

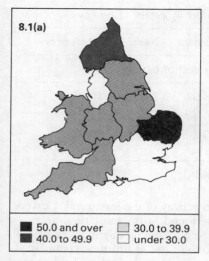

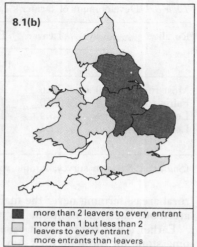

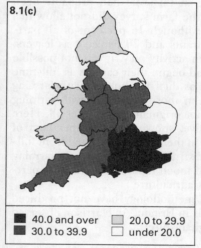

Fig. 8.1 Regional variations in development of part-time farmers' careers.

(a) Percentage with farming always the main occupation.

(b) Relative importance of 'leavers' and 'entrants' among part-time farmers.

(c) Percentage for whom farming has never been the main occupation.

to be more prevalent in the north-west and south-west of England. The farmer's career was one of the few variables which proved to be significantly related to the degree of rurality. According to Table 8.4, farming always being the main activity is characteristic of the more

Table 8.4 Development of farmer's career by degree of rurality

Rurality	Always	Leaver	Entrant	Never	All farmers
			per cent of farmers		
Most rural	52.0	19.6	14.0	14.4	100.0
Fairly rural	51.4	11.0	16.8	20.8	100.0
Less rural	46.4	13.4	16.2	24.0	100.0
Least rural	36.6	17.2	17.2	29.0	100.0 **

(*Source*: 1984 farm survey, sample results)

rural areas, farming never the main activity of the least rural. Leavers are more likely than entrants to be found in the most rural areas.

Earlier it was suggested that part-time farming might act as a stepping stone for those on their way into or out of full-time commercial agriculture but that its importance in this role had probably been exaggerated. The data collected in the farm survey did not allow this proposition to be tested precisely. Although 15 per cent of all part-time farmers were described as entrants and 20 per cent as leavers, this referred to a change in the main activity only. It was not possible to distinguish between those who had begun their careers as full-time farmers and those who had started as dual-job holders with farming as the main occupation, nor between those beginning with farming as a subsidiary activity and those not originally farming at all. Here the pilot study was more informative, showing that 22 per cent of part-time farmers had at some stage in their careers changed from full- to part-time farming. (Samples drawn from those currently farming part time could not, of course, shed much light on moves from part-time to full-time farming or out of agriculture.)

Studies using more appropriate methodology have not produced strong support for the mobility thesis in Britain. As Harrison observed in his study of farming in Buckinghamshire:

> The change from part to full-time farming, or vice versa, can effect a significant change in altering the pattern of resource and effort deployment. It could for example provide an important line of recruitment for full-time farmers. But it does not seem to be used very much in this way. The majority of part-time farmers have had another source of earned income during their entire farming career. There was never at any time, any plan to become a full-time farmer (Harrison 1966:16–17).

While many operators enter full-time farming in Canada via the part-time route, more enter full-time farming directly (Bollman and Steeves,

1980). Few full-time farmers appear to use part-time farming as a stage on the way out of agriculture according to the evidence from Canada (Bollman 1982) and Sweden (Bolin and Persson 1978). On balance more families probably enter than leave the industry by this route. Bollman concluded that having another job probably retarded exit but assisted entry to agriculture. Nalson (1968:119–124) too saw part-time farming as an avenue through which outsiders entered the industry. In Staffordshire he identified three categories of recruits to part-time farming: those who saw it as a first step on the farming ladder, those who were content to remain as part-time farmers and those using the farm as a temporary refuge, some of whom were transients attracted by the cheap housing and remoteness of an isolated farm.

MEANS OF ACQUIRING THE HOLDING

People entering farming at different stages in their careers might well have acquired their farms by different means. If, for instance, purchase of a holding depends on accumulating savings from another job, it could be expected to occur quite late in a person's career. Respondents in the farm survey were asked how the present holding had been acquired. Where parcels of land were acquired by different means, the question referred to the largest fragment. From the replies it was estimated that 57 per cent of all part-time farmers had bought their holdings, 26 per cent had inherited and 18 per cent rented them under normal agricultural tenancies. Small numbers who had bought as sitting tenants, usually at the beginning of their period of occupancy, were included with the purchasers. Those taking over tenancies from relatives on preferential terms were included with the inheritors.

The larger the holding, the more likely was the farmer to have inherited or rented it in the first place, the less likely to have bought it. This relationship was highly significant with the sharpest distinction between band 1 holdings and the rest. Two-thirds of the farms in band 1 had been bought by the present occupiers compared with less than half in any other band. The association with income class was even stronger. According to Table 8.5, purchase was particularly important in Class IIb, implying that few occupiers of this type had the opportunity to inherit or rent farms. It also fits in with the suggestion in Chapter 7 that investment may be an important motive for some members of Class II and especially IIb. Farmers in Class I and IIa were much more likely than IIb to have inherited, which implies a farming background. Renting land, which suggests a serious commitment to farming for profit and that the farmer appears to be

Table 8.5 Means of acquiring present holding by income class

Income class	Purchased	Inherited	Rented	All holdings
		per cent of holdings		
I	40.2	34.7	25.1	100.0
IIa	51.9	31.6	16.5	100.0
IIb	73.0	13.5	13.5	100.0 ***

(*Source*: 1984 farm survey, sample results)

a desirable tenant, was most common for members of Class I. Similar conclusions were drawn from Table 7.3 which showed how land was held by the three classes. Further analysis confirmed the link between the way the farmer's career had developed and how the farm was acquired. Farming had been the first occupation chronologically for 75 per cent of those who had inherited the present holding and for 80 per cent of those renting but for fewer than half of those who had purchased their farms.

Regional differences in the way holdings were acquired were also highly significant (Fig. 8.2). Buying a farm, likely to be the only option for those new to agriculture from non-farming backgrounds, was the main means in every region but especially important in the south-east of England and the West Midlands. Inheritance was most prevalent in the East Midlands, East Anglia and Wales while renting was a particular feature of the three northern regions.

SUCCESSION PLANS

One key to the farmer's future intentions must be his plan for succession. On the basis of the farm survey it was estimated that 40 per cent of all occupiers on part-time farms expected to hand them on to family successors while 32 per cent definitely did not and 28 per cent were uncertain. The proportion of respondents in the farm survey expecting successors was higher than the 30 per cent in the pilot study but lower than the 44 per cent among small-scale beef and sheep farmers in the Northern Ireland study (Moss 1980:41) or the 62 per cent among part-time farmers in the Irish Republic (Higgins 1983:53). Succession is still more likely to occur on full-time farms however. Harrison (1975:28) estimated that 76 per cent of all English farmers required successors and that of these, nine out of ten had a successor already identified, ready and able to take over the running of the farm.

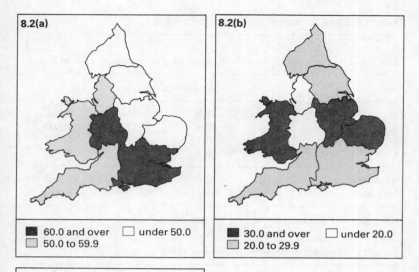

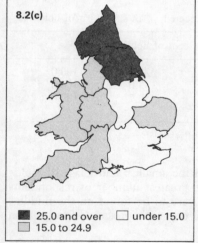

Fig. 8.2 Means of acquiring part-time holdings.
(a) Percentage of holdings purchased.
(b) Percentage of holdings inherited.
(c) Percentage of holdings rented.

The size of the farm business and its income-generating capacity appear to be the main influences on succession plans. As Tables 8.6 and 8.7 show, more than half the occupiers of the largest and Class I part-time holdings expected to hand them on to successors compared

Table 8.6 Plans for succession by size of holding

Size band	Successor expected	Not expected	Not sure	All holdings
		per cent of holdings		
1	34.8	39.0	26.2	100.0
2	38.2	30.4	31.4	100.0
3	42.7	23.4	33.9	100.0
4	55.4	16.8	27.8	100.0
All holdings	39.6	32.0	28.4	100.0 ***
Numbers	20 722 *a*	16 763 *b*	14 859 *b*	52 344

(*Source*: 1984 farm survey, raised results)

Table 8.7 Plans for succession by income class

Income class	Successor expected	Not expected	Not sure	All holdings
		per cent of holdings		
I	52.2	20.6	27.2	100.0
IIa	37.8	29.2	33.0	100.0
IIb	30.1	39.2	30.7	100.0 ***

(*Source*: 1984 farm survey, sample results)

with only about a third of those on the smallest and Class IIb holdings. It may be significant that the greatest number of respondents who felt unsure about succession were to be found on the middle-sized and Class IIa holdings, where economic prospects for the farm business would be the least clearcut.

The larger the farm, the more attractive it would be as an inheritance and, other things being equal, the more the heir would be prepared to sacrifice in order to acquire it. If the business is too small to allow the farmer and his successor to work together one of them (often the successor) will have to find other employment. Having experienced other work, a different lifestyle and a regular wage packet, the successor may be less inclined to return home to farm. Besides this, occupiers of smaller part-time holdings usually have other main occupations and their children may choose to follow them into the other job rather than take over the farm business. The farm survey revealed a strong tendency for farming to continue in those families where it had originally been dominant. Nearly half the farmers who had started their careers in agriculture but fewer than a third of the rest expected to hand the farm on to a successor eventually. The way the holding had been acquired also had a bearing on the way the farmer intended to dispose of it; over half of those who had inherited the present holding but only about 40 per cent of those who had purchased or rented in the first place expected to hand it on to the next generation.

Regional variations in succession plans may have been a reflection of the stronger farming orientation in the north of England than in the south. In the north region 64 per cent of farmers expected to have successors, in the south-east only 24 per cent. These findings seem to correspond with regional differences in family structure which were discussed in Chapter 3 and summarised in Table 3.4. A stronger tendency for farming to continue in families in northern England than in the south might explain why there are more part-time farming families in the early and middle stages of the family cycle in the north and more incomplete families in the south.

YEAR OF ENTRY TO THE HOLDING

The case for a life-history approach to the study of part-time farming appears to be justified. Close associations have been found between such aspects of the present situation as farm size, income class and the nature of the other occupation, and variables reflecting the way the farmer's career had developed, such as whether it began in agriculture, whether farming was ever intended to be the main activity and how the holding was acquired. These associations add a new perspective and contribute towards an understanding of the present situation. One drawback of the life-cycle approach is that events are being compared which occurred at different points in history. Farmers who took part in the survey ranged from under twenty-five to over eighty years of age, implying that their entry to the labour force spanned a period of more than fifty years. Different patterns of career development would therefore be reflecting changes in the wider economic environment, for example in availability of employment off the farm, as well as circumstances internal to the farm household. In an attempt to overcome this problem and relate events in the farmer's life to the passage of time, respondents were asked when the farmer had taken over the present holding on his own account. Where there were several partners the question was addressed to the principal occupier and where parcels of land had been acquired at different times, the question referred to the piece acquired first.

The oldest farmer interviewed in 1984 had started farming his present farm in 1922. As Table 8.8 shows, 21 per cent of occupiers had taken over their present holdings before 1960 but, at the other extreme, 16 per cent had only come since the beginning of 1980 and 56 per cent since 1970. This agrees quite well with Harrison's estimate that 52 per cent of part-time farmers in England had entered their present farms within the previous 15 years (Harrison 1975:17).

Table 8.8 Distribution of part-time farmers by period of entry to present holding

Period of entry	Estimated numbers	Per cent
Pre-1960	10 987 b	21.0
1960–69	11 985 b	22.9
1970–74	7 216 b	13.8
1975–79	13 849 b	26.4
1980–84	8 307 b	15.9
All farmers	52 344	100.0

(*Source*: 1984 farm survey, raised results)

Period of entry is significantly associated with farm size; the larger the holding, the longer the farmer is likely to have occupied it.

More than 20 per cent of occupiers in band 1 but only 9 per cent in bands 3 and 4 had come since the beginning of 1980 (Table 8.9). This cannot be attributed to size-related variations in the farmer's age or stage in the family cycle since farm size showed no significant association with either.

Table 8.9 Period of entry by size of holding

Size band	Pre-1970	1970 to 1979	1980 to 1984	All farmers
		per cent of farmers		
1	39.1	40.4	20.5	100.0
2	43.9	43.8	12.3	100.0
3	49.7	41.0	9.3	100.0
4	56.2	34.6	9.2	100.0
All holdings	43.9	40.2	15.9	100.0 **

(*Source*: 1984 farm survey, raised results)

Period of entry to the holding was still more closely linked to income class. Table 8.10 shows the income-class composition of each entry cohort. It shows that more than half of all part-time farmers who took over their present holdings before 1970 were members of Class I. The more recently was the holding acquired, the more prominent are Class II part-time farmers relative to Class I. By extension, it could be predicted that part-time farming families would have entered agriculture more recently, on average, than full-time. Confirmation of this comes from Buckinghamshire (Harrison 1967:6) and from the United States (Lyson 1984) where part-time farmers are more prominent among recent entrants to farming than in the farm population as a whole.

Table 8.10 Period of entry by income class

Period of entry	Class I	Class IIa	Class IIb	All holdings
		per cent of farmers		
Pre-1960	61.9	23.9	14.2	100.0
1960–69	55.2	26.2	18.6	100.0
1970–74	43.6	37.3	19.1	100.0
1975–79	37.8	28.0	34.2	100.0
1980–84	28.9	37.8	33.3	100.0
				***

(*Source*: 1984 farm survey, sample results)

Further evidence of a link between a farming background and orientation and length of occupancy is provided by Table 8.11. The more recently the holding was acquired, the less likely it was that the

Table 8.11 Period of entry and development of farmer's career

Period of entry	Per cent of farmers for whom farming was:	
	first occupation	intended to be main occupation
Pre-1960	79.5	83.2
1960–69	70.0	76.2
1970–74	69.1	71.8
1975–79	43.5	62.9
1980–84	45.5	51.1
	***	***

(*Source*: 1984 farm survey, sample results)

farmer had started his working life in agriculture or that he had entered the holding with the intention of making farming his main occupation. In other words, recent years have seen an influx of farm occupiers who, by comparison with those already established, are newcomers to farming and who do not see themselves as farmers first and foremost.

The way in which the farmer acquired the holding also varies significantly with the period of entry (Table 8.12). Rented holdings have been in the hands of their present occupiers for longest on average and purchased holdings have been acquired the most recently. This fits in with the general trend for few farms to be available for renting nowadays. Those who wish to start farming and are not in the fortunate position of inheriting land are therefore obliged to purchase. The data would also be consistent with the suggestion that soaring land prices and high interest rates in recent years have resulted in more financial failures and hence a higher rate of turnover on farms which have been purchased than on inherited or rented farms. Yet another explanation would link the findings to the idea that a new type of person is coming into agriculture. This idea is explored in the next section.

Table 8.12 Period of entry and means of acquiring the holding

Period of entry	Purchased	Inherited	Rented
	per cent of holdings		
Pre-1970	40.4	52.6	58.7
1970–79	43.8	35.7	33.3
1980–84	15.8	11.7	8.0
All holdings	100.0	100.0	100.0 ***

(*Source*: 1984 farm survey, sample results)

INTERPRETING THE RESULTS

The population of part-time farming families seems to be separating into two main clusters according to the way the farmer's career has developed. Typical of the first group are those from farming backgrounds who began their working lives in agriculture and inherited or took over a family tenancy on the present holding. Many of these farmers expect their sons to continue farming after them. Farming the holding is the main activity and principal source of household income. The other activity is likely to be work on other farms or a farm-based enterprise, not necessarily run by the farmer himself. Households displaying many of these characteristics are in a majority on the larger farms and are well represented in northern and eastern England.

The typical occupier of the second group began farming later in life, having already embarked on some other career or built up another business. Farming has never been more than a secondary activity and source of income, the household depending mainly on off-farm employment or possibly a home business. Farmers in this position usually had to buy their holdings. The economic bonds and family ties with the land or with a particular holding which characterise long-established farming families are absent, so there is no strong incentive for the younger generation to continue farming; in fact only a minority of farmers in this group expect their sons to follow in their footsteps. Part-time farming families of this type predominate in band 1, which is the largest group numerically, and are especially prevalent in southern England and the north-west. Part-time farming in Sweden is similarly dominated by one group of part-time farmers who are mainly occupied in agriculture and who are acquiring an increasing share of the arable land, and another group of 'hobby farmers' mainly occupied off the farm, who farm in their leisure time and are increasing in numbers (Bolin and Persson 1978).

These contrasting types of part-time farmer are really 'ideal types' devised to aid understanding but not necessarily corresponding to actual cases. It would be naive to suggest that all part-time farming households could be allocated to one group or the other. While any individual case which shares some characteristics of one group will be likely to correspond in other respects, there may be households which do not fit easily into either camp. Often in an equivocal position are households in Class IIa and those on the smaller Class I holdings, those in bands 2 and 3 and the transitional groups of entrants and leavers.

The chronological analysis adds a new dimension. Significant associations have been found between most of the 'career' variables and period of entry to the holding. Those who took over their present holdings earlier, and notably before 1970, include a majority of the Class I type of family with farming roots. Among those starting to farm the present holding more recently are a majority of the Class II type for whom farming has never been the main activity or source of income. These farmers and their families are less likely than the first group to have come from farming backgrounds or to have begun their careers in agriculture. This discovery is open to various explanations.

Changes in the structure of agriculture

The findings are in line with broad trends in the structure of agriculture which were discussed at the beginning of this chapter. Over time the farm-rooted, farm-oriented Class I type of part-time farming family is giving way to the Class II type from a different background, for whom farming is always going to remain secondary to the main activity. To press the point further, Table 8.1 suggested that in England and Wales Class IIb may be increasing relative to Class IIa. Growing emphasis on the Class II type of part-time farming household can be seen as one manifestation of the declining importance of agriculture in the economy of developed countries. It will be likely to mean a growing dependence of farm families in general on non-farm sources of income, a blurring of rural–urban differences and a gradual disappearance of any distinct farming group in the population.

This kind of macro-level interpretation is entirely consistent with the facts but it stops short of explaining how the change comes about. The switch from full-time to part-time farming and from Class I to Class II part-time farming might occur within the career of the individual farmer, within the family, at the point of inter-generational transfer or when the holding changes hands (Gasson 1986). In practice all these types of change are probably occurring at the same time, though not necessarily to the same extent. Different types of change may predominate at different periods. In Poland, for example, the dominant trend before 1960 was for peasants to be transformed into peasant workers. More recently the main development has been for younger members of the farm family still living on the holding and helping their parents, to seek non-farm jobs (Kłodziński 1983).

For England and Wales the most obvious form of change would be for operators of progressively larger full-time farms to seek alternative sources of income, thereby moving into Class I part-time farming and for smaller Class I part-time farms to become Class II. Although the farm surveys did not address this question directly, available evidence suggests that changes within the individual farmer's career are not the main route into part-time farming in this country. The pilot study found that only about one part-time farmer in five had previously farmed full time whereas up to half of them had taken over the present holding from a full-time farmer. Fewer had replaced other part-time farmers. The change to part-time farming often seems to occur at the point of succession; in the Irish studies a majority of farmers with successors in prospect expected their successors to have off-farm jobs (Moss 1980:41; Higgins 1983:54). The growing tendency for farmers' wives to enter the labour force is also helping to transform the structure of agriculture in Britain (Gasson 1984). A paid job was recorded for the spouse on less than 5 per cent of all agricultural holdings in England and Wales in the 1980 LII but on over 11 per cent in the 1983 LII.

Conditions favouring part-time farming

Another possibility is that circumstances in the past ten to fifteen years have favoured the entry to agriculture of families from non-farm backgrounds with other main occupations and income sources whereas conditions before about 1970 were more favourable towards the entry of those with farming as the main activity. Such circumstances might include declining farm incomes, the shrinking supply of farms to rent and rising farm land prices, which would have the effect of squeezing the marginal full-time and Class I type of part-time farmer. At the same time high rates of inflation coupled with rising land prices have made land an attractive investment for those with access to capital funds and other income sources. The growth of the environmental movement and population shifts towards rural areas may have given further encouragement to the Class II type of part-time farming family.

This kind of short-to-medium-term trend has been observed before. At the end of the Second World War a number of influences including a resurgence of fundamentalist values and generous tax allowances encouraged the entry to agriculture of the hobby farmer but within a few years conditions had become more favourable to the establishment, enlargement and consolidation of the full-time commercial farm business. During periods of agricultural depression farmers with other sources of income tend to be the survivors. In the Kent and East Sussex study, for example, full-time farmers were found to have been in their farms for longer, on average, than part-time farmers in the mid-1960s whereas in the early 1940s it was the part-time farmers who had been established the longest (Gasson 1966:28–9). If the changes occurring since 1970 are assumed to be exceptional but temporary, a return to a more farm-oriented type of part-time farming might be predicted under a different political and economic regime.

Differential rates of turnover

A third possibility is that the rate of turnover is greater among part-time than full-time farming families and greater among Class II than Class I. In other words the kind of part-time farmer who comes from a non-farm background and does not depend on farming for his livelihood does not stay in one place for long. Lacking experience of farm life, it may prove to be less rewarding, more time-consuming or a bigger drain on resources than expected. The farmer may be a 'spiralist' for whom promotion in the main job usually entails moving to another part of the country or even overseas. Living on a farm may be a temporary expedient suiting the family's needs for a short period. One couple in the farm survey had bought a small holding in response to a teenage daughter's craze for horse-riding and were somewhat at a loss to know what to do with it when the daughter left home to train as a nurse. Another illustration was provided by a successful businessman who had tasted and enjoyed the experience of life on a small farm to the full but had since tired of it and was planning to sell the farm so that he could savour a different lifestyle. Where farming is the main activity, as for Class I and full-time farmers, the family is expected to remain on the same holding for much longer, being more committed to agriculture, more likely to have farming roots and family ties with the industry and to produce farming heirs. Such families have much more to lose by giving up the farm and the alternatives may appear unattractive to them.

While each explanation appears to be consistent with the observed facts, each would have a different outcome. Information collected in the farm surveys is not adequate to decide between the three levels of explanation, the first relating to long-term and permanent transformations in the economy and structure of agriculture, the second to reversible short- or medium-term trends in the economy, the third to influences largely internal to the family. Each explanation probably carries some truth and they need not be mutually exclusive. While the population of part-time farming families may be turning over quite rapidly, and Class II more rapidly than Class I, the part-time sector as a whole may be growing and veering more towards Class II. Whether this is a long-term immutable trend or of shorter duration and reversible, only time will tell.

Motivation of part-time farmers

GOALS OF PART-TIME FARMERS

Farming is a business subject to market forces like any other. The farmer as an entrepreneur needs to be aware of the margin between costs and returns, the rate of return on capital, the opportunity cost of his labour and managerial input and of the capital invested in the business. It does not follow that economic considerations like these must necessarily dominate the farmer's thinking to the exclusion of all else.

To people in most occupations, work means much more than just earning a living. Keeping healthy and interested, enjoying the activity itself, being associated with others, gaining recognition and prestige, fostering self-respect and justifying one's existence are some of the reasons for which people work and for which they would continue to work even if it were no longer financially necessary. To most farmers, the economic or instrumental motives for continuing in the occupation are interwoven with a rich diversity of social, intrinsic and expressive goals. Farmers as a group place a high value on intrinsic aspects of the work itself such as independence, the healthy open-air life, living in the countryside and seeing things grow. Expressive aspects, such as meeting a challenge, taking a gamble, achieving an objective and being creative, are valued highly by many farmers. Even among the more mundane instrumental concerns, making a satisfactory income in the present and ensuring a reasonable and secure income in the future may be preferred to maximising current income. Intrinsic values appear to be especially important for occupiers of smaller farms, goals like maximising income and expanding the business assuming greater salience for operators of larger holdings (Gasson 1973).

If motives other than maximising farm income are important for full-time commercial farmers, they are likely to be still more so for part-time farmers who do not depend wholly on farming for a living. Bollman (1979: Appendix D) concluded from a review of the North American literature that part-time farmers were motivated by a preference for rural living as well as by the need to supplement family income. A study of part-time farmers in the Vosges indicated the importance of fulfilling ethical goals. There farmers stressed the values of their way of life which involved direct responsibilities and creative leisure, comparing it favourably with the lifestyle of employees who had no initiative in their work and spent their leisure time in boredom in front of the television (Brun 1977:63).

To explore the motivations of part-time farmers in England and Wales, respondents in the farm survey were asked to rate the importance of five aspects of the farming occupation from their own point of view. As Table 9.1 shows, four out of five rated 'living in the countryside' and 'job satisfaction in farming' as very important to them personally. Fewer than half regarded 'making the best possible income from farming' as very important. For the sample as a whole the income goal was rated lower than 'nature conservation on the farm' but higher than 'having capital invested in land'. The same question in the pilot study produced a very similar response with the same ordering of goals. The attribute of 'having the family continue in farming' was dropped from the list for the main survey as only 17 per cent of pilot study respondents rated it as important.

Table 9.1 Importance attached to farming goals by part-time farmers

Goal	Rated as 'very important' by	per cent	Per cent in pilot study
Living in the countryside	42 122	80.5	80.9
Job satisfaction in farming	41 572	79.4	78.6
Conservation on the farm	24 579	47.0	38.2
Best income from farming	22 821	43.6	36.9
Capital invested in land	17 011	32.5	32.5

(*Source*: 1984 farm survey, raised results and pilot study)

These findings are broadly in line with other studies where farmers give higher verbal ratings to intrinsic aspects of the farming occupation than to income and capital considerations. While most farmers

would probably subscribe to most of the dominant values most of the
time in some degree, it is the relative ordering of values or goals which
produces in each individual or group of individuals a distinctive
character and propensity to act. Differences between categories of
farmers are therefore of more interest than similarities between them.
Motives may well vary between those part-time farmers who have
diversified from full-time farming and those who are new entrants to
agriculture; the former might be expected to place a higher value on
supplementing family income, the latter on rural living. Dependence
on farming as a source of income is also likely to be reflected in value
orientations. For members of Class IIb in particular, the attractions
of a farming lifestyle are likely to figure large. There have been
several indications already that owning land may be more important
for some members of this class than farming it.

In the United States Coughenour and Christenson (1981:12)
found significant differences in value orientations between part-time
farmers in white-collar and blue-collar occupations. In the present
study income class and the development of the farmer's career were
the best predictors of motivation. All groups of part-time farmers
attached a high value to living in the countryside and professed little
interest in the investment motive but quite sharp differences emerged
in respect of the remaining goals (Table 9.2). Job satisfaction in
farming was valued significantly higher by operators of the larger,
Class I holdings and where farming was currently the farmer's main
activity. Making the best possible income from farming followed
the same pattern with particularly low ratings from occupiers of the

Table 9.2 Importance attached to farming goals by income class and
development of farmer's career

Class	Job satisfaction	Best farm income	Nature conservation
	per cent rating this as 'very important'		
I	86.7	66.9	40.8
IIa	76.2	44.6	43.7
IIb	77.3	36.2	49.6
	***	***	ns
Farmer's main occupation			
Always farming	87.5	65.0	40.4
Entrant	86.6	56.2	49.1
Leaver	74.7	43.9	39.3
Never farming	69.5	32.5	50.0
	***	***	*

(*Source*: 1984 farm survey, sample results)

smallest, Class IIb holdings and where farming had never been the main activity. The importance attached to nature conservation on the farm showed the opposite tendency, being more important (but not significantly so) in Class II than in Class I and for those never farming as the main occupation than for those always farming. On this occasion the leavers had most in common with those always farming and entrants with those never farming, suggesting that it is the farmer's background and past experience rather than his present commitment which is the formative influence in his attitude towards nature conservation.

Motives of Wisconsin part-time farmers showed a similar pattern of variation by family background. The main reasons given by transitional and persistent part-time farmers for taking up off-farm employment were to finance farm investment and to make a living because the farm was too small. Wives or sons wishing to pursue careers of their own was another common response for these groups. Among those who had come into agriculture more recently, entrants in particular mentioned 'enjoyment of country life' and 'dislike of the city environment' as their main reasons for farming. Wisconsin U-turn part-time farmers, those who had previous experience of both farming and non-farm work, showed a strong preference for farm work and wanted to combine it with their other job. Some mentioned motives of investment and security but relatively few put forward 'seeking farm income' as a reason for acquiring the farm (Kada 1980).

REACTIONS TO FALLING FARM INCOMES

If attitudes and values are propensities to act, then knowledge of the importance attached to values in the farming occupation could be used to predict how farmers will behave. Pursuing this idea, respondents were asked how they would react if returns from farming were to fall drastically, say by at least a third. Imposition of milk quotas in the spring of 1984, just before interviewing for the main survey began, had made this a very real threat for some of them. Replies to the question were recorded verbatim and later coded under four headings:

Adjust through farming – make changes within the existing farm business by tightening up efficiency, increasing output, cutting costs, moving to a different farming system, buying a larger farm, introducing new and more profitable enterprises or giving up less profitable ones.

Adjust through other activities – compensate for lower farm income by earning more from an existing non-farm or off-farm occupation or enterprise or by starting some new venture.

Give up farming – retire, sell the farm, give up tenancy of the present holding, let the land but continue living in the farmhouse.

No change – little or no change in the present farming system would be necessary because farming is not essential to household income; in a few cases change was not considered to be feasible owing to constraints of high altitude, difficult soils or terrain, a small acreage or heavy investment in a particular type of farming.

The largest number of replies in Table 9.3 have to do with making changes in the farming system. Roughly equal numbers suggested compensating by means of another activity, giving up farming or carrying on just as before. Replies to the same question in the pilot study three years earlier were much less positive. On that occasion 46 per cent of respondents considered that no change in farming would be necessary and fewer were prepared to consider making adjustments to their farming or other activities or giving up farming altogether. It seems possible that the threat of milk quotas and the looming crisis over the Common Agricultural Policy had sharpened the minds of many farmers to the real possibility of a drop in incomes and that more serious thought had been given to the alternatives.

Table 9.3 Reactions to a hypothetical drop in farm incomes by income class and development of farmer's career

Class	Adjust through farming	Adjust through other activity	Give up farming	No change	Total
		per cent of responses			
I	37.2	27.2	22.0	13.6	100.0
IIa	24.6	24.6	24.6	26.2	100.0
IIb	22.3	15.0	27.5	35.2	100.0 ***
Farmer's main occupation					
Always farming	33.7	26.3	23.9	16.1	100.0
Entrant	30.8	25.7	27.0	16.5	100.0
Leaver	27.5	18.3	22.9	31.3	100.0
Never farming	23.2	18.5	21.5	36.8	100.0 ***
All replies	30.3	23.8	24.1	21.8	100.0

(*Source*: 1984 farm survey, sample results)

The way part-time farmers responded to the question varied very significantly between size bands and regions, between income classes and according to the farmer's work history. To ignore a drop in farm income and carry on much as before was the typical reaction of those who were least dependent on farming for employment and income. More than a third of the part-time farmers in band 1, Class IIb and among those never farming as the main occupation, give this response. Presumably reliance on another income source would cushion them from financial hardship. How long they could afford to ignore market forces would be another matter. Table 9.3 suggests that the next response, at least for those in Class IIb, would be to give up farming.

Those mainly dependent on farm incomes and employment were much more inclined to try other ways of making the farm pay. This was the first reaction of a third or more of those in bands 3 and 4, in the north region, in Class I and where farming had always been the main occupation. Trying to adjust by means of some other enterprise came next in importance for those on the largest and Class I holdings, for those always farming and particularly in south-west England (the dairy quota and the tourist enterprise?). In answering this question as on other occasions, members of Class IIa appeared to be somewhat equivocal, neither firmly committed to the farm business approach nor yet so financially secure that they could afford to ignore it.

PURSUIT OF OTHER GOALS

Farmers who are cushioned from market forces by another income source may choose to pursue non-financial goals through their farming activities. From the Kent and East Sussex survey it appeared that while full-time farmers were on the whole striving for economic efficiency, part-timers were often more interested in technical efficiency. Their goals might be to market an attractive product, to keep the property in tip-top order, to achieve the highest yields in the district, to breed prizewinning livestock or to overcome some technical problem. One part-time farmer, for example – an engineer in a defence establishment – was trying to perfect the design of a potato harvester. To attain such ends the part-time farmers might need to employ more labour, invest more in buildings or machinery, spend more on repairs and maintenance than would be justified on a full-time farm. Even in the mid-1960s only the wealthiest part-time farmers could still afford the luxury of 'high farming'.

Brun (1977:68) attributes this innovativeness to the deep ideological and psychological motives which impel some individuals to become part-time farmers under difficult conditions. He observed that part-time farmers in less favoured areas of France were extremely inventive in their efforts to create new jobs for members of the family, in developing sidelines on the farm and in the ways they organised farm work and family life. Examples included expanding the demand for farm products by bringing new products before a wider group of consumers and providing new services such as farm holidays, minding children and caretaking for second homes.

Conservation of the natural environment is another goal which may be pursued more enthusiastically by those not wholly dependent on the farm for their livelihood. Table 9.2 gave a hint of this but the idea was strongly supported in the pilot study where the issue was explored rather more fully. At that time the 'farming versus wildlife' debate was already in full swing. Farmers in general seemed very sensitive to charges of causing environmental damage and, in that sample at least, more than ready to discuss their views on conservation. A majority of those interviewed expressed themselves 'strongly in favour' (38 per cent) or 'somewhat in favour' (38 per cent) of nature conservation on the farm. Fewer than 5 per cent were 'somewhat against' or 'strongly against' introducing conservation practices in agriculture. Even so, only about two respondents in five claimed to have taken positive steps to conserve or enhance the natural environment on their own farms in the previous five years and only about one in four had firm plans to take such action in the next year or two. The most popular conservation practices seemed to be planting trees and digging ponds or preserving what was already there by retaining hedgerows and trees and not draining wet land. Few had gone to the extreme of organic forming but a number were consciously trying to avoid excessive use of chemicals on the farm.

Table 9.4 illustrates a considerable divergence of views on conservation according to the farmer's background in the pilot study sample, a tendency which was only weakly apparent in Table 9.2. The group of entrants who came into agriculture from some other main occupation but now regard farming as their main activity have much more in common with those who have never farmed as the main activity than with those always putting farming first. According to Table 9.4, 54 per cent of entrants expressed themselves strongly in favour of conservation on the farm as against only 23 per cent of those always farming. Leavers in this case appear to be less 'conservation minded' than the sample as a whole but somewhat more positive than those for whom farming continues to be the main concern. Differences in respect of the main source of income were less marked but generally in the expected direction; members of Class IIb were the most strongly in favour of conservation and the most likely to back up words with actions while members of Class I tended to be the least positive.

Recent research in London's Green Belt also suggests a link

Table 9.4 Approach to conservation by income class and development of farmer's career

Class	Strongly in favour of conservation	Taken positive action	Plans to take action
	per cent of farmers		
I	25.8	40.3	29.0
IIa	36.6	45.4	27.3
IIb	42.1	46.1	32.9
	ns	**	*
Farmer's main occupation			
Always farming	23.4	26.1	19.8
Leaver	29.9	35.6	23.0
Entrant	53.7	49.3	31.3
Never farming	43.3	50.7	32.0
	***	***	*
All farmers	38.2	40.5	26.5

(*Source*: pilot study)

between the degree of landscape change and the degree to which development of the farming enterprise is essential for survival or expansion of the farm business. Loss of hedgerows was greatest on full-time farms and on those where the occupier had been diversifying the income sources as a means of keeping the family enterprise viable. Least change was reported on hobby farms, here defined as businesses where 90 per cent or more of the income is from off-farm sources (Muntc n *et al.* 1985).

BENEFITS AND DRAWBACKS OF PART-TIME FARMING

Combining the running of a farm business with other gainful activities will most probably mean both benefits and drawbacks for the families concerned. A higher and more stable income for the household is likely to be the main advantage in many cases but, as this chapter has indicated, income is not the only motivating force. Chapter 5 pointed out that a majority of part-time farmers run second businesses which implies conflict over the allocation of funds and competing claims on the proprietor's time. The fact that the other activities of farmers are more likely than not to be linked to farming in some way suggests that benefits will flow in both directions.

Respondents in the pilot study were asked whether each occupation brought benefits and drawbacks for the other. Two points stand out clearly from Table 9.5. First, more respondents mentioned benefits than drawbacks in part-time farming and second, farming appeared to be affected by other occupations to a greater extent than it affected them.

Table 9.5 Perceived relationships between farming and other activities

Nature of relationship	Per cent of positive responses
Farming benefits from other activity	74.2
Farming suffers from other activity	31.4
Other activity benefits from farming	40.7
Other activity suffers from farming	17.4

(*Source*: pilot study)

More positive than negative replies could have been predicted from the way the question was posed. Interviewed in their own homes by strangers, respondents may have felt constrained to keep the tone of their comments as pleasant as possible, suppressing any complaints about their part-time farming experiences. Besides this, where part-time farming represents a conscious choice, respondents could be expected to evaluate it positively. To suggest that on balance it had brought more disadvantages than benefits would be to admit that they had made a bad decision. This would not apply so much in the case of those who did not feel they were responsible for the decision to farm part-time, for instance those squeezed out of full-time farming or members of farmers' families, some of whom had to bear a heavy burden of extra work. Such individuals might be expected to dwell on the drawbacks of part-time farming rather more freely.

Kada's study provides oblique support for this idea. Among his Wisconsin part-time farmers, it was the entrants and U-turn groups and farmers in professional and managerial posts who were the most likely to perceive the two occupations as being complementary. Conflict in the relationship was more likely to be mentioned by transitional and persistent part-time farmers and by those with other manual jobs (Kada 1980:112). In the pilot study, too, the proportion of farmers who perceived benefits for both farming and the other occupation rose to a maximum in the top farm size band. On the largest holdings which should be capable of supporting a family at a satisfactory level of living, it is inferred that the second activity would be an expression of choice, for example allowing the farmer's wife or another family member to pursue a preferred career.

The suggestion that farming was affected more by the existence of another job than the other job was affected by farming, can be readily understood. The majority of families interviewed depended mainly on the other activity for income and devoted most time to it. A number of them had entered farming quite recently, making little or no change in the previous occupation. Asked whether the other activity suffered in any way from farming, the most common reply was 'I cannot afford to let it.' Particularly at a time of high unemployment and falling farm incomes, those mainly dependent on their other occupations would be ill advised to put the farm first.

In the main survey respondents were asked to describe particular benefits and drawbacks that the family had experienced as a result of part-time farming. The examples quoted below illustrate some of the perceived benefits, with income considerations heading the list.

Providing income

'Income is the only reason – gives us enough to live on – other income allows us to stay on the farm – diversifying our activities is a kind of insurance – provides financial security for our young family – we can enjoy the same standard of living as urban folk.'

Capital appreciation

'Farming is only a means of investing in land – asset appreciation – income from the other job is ploughed back into farming – we have more to spend on farm improvements – it allows us to make a derelict farm into a viable proposition.'

Employment

'Keeps all the family interested and on the farm – provides a job for my son who is not interested in farming – we see less of our son now, which is counted as a blessing – gets me out of the way so that my son can have his head for a few days.'

Social contact

'We enjoy contact with people – both of us make new friends through our work – social life is improved because the wife's income allows us to go out more.'

Complementary relationships

'Other activity gives us an outlet for our farm produce – cheaper supplies for our farm shop/cafe – profitable use of surplus cottages – better use of labour in slack periods – access to skills and tools which are useful for farm maintenance – we can justify more expenditure on machinery – people are more ready to approach me as a vet/auctioneer/consultant because they know that I am also a farmer.'

Information

'I keep learning through meeting other farmers – I've learnt a lot about farming through contacts made as a milk recorder – seeing how neighbours do things – wife/daughter keeps us up to date with tax/financial matters – outside contacts keep farming on the top line.'

Interest

'The farm/the other job provides a new interest – a hobby for retirement – keeps you physically and mentally fit in retirement – broadens one's outlook – keeps me sane – keeps the wife sane – teaching gives my wife a degree of independence and mental stimulation – wife is much happier now she is out to work again.'

Lifestyle

'Amenity value of the farm – it's a healthier life – a more humane life – quality of life – way of life – a means of living in the countryside – I value the privacy afforded by having two separate lives – we enjoy farming more because we do not depend on the income.'

Perceived benefits of part-time farming differed significantly between the income classes and in respect of the farmer's background, these differences being greater than those associated with the size of the holding. According to Table 9.6, income and capital considerations came first with every group except where farming had never been the main activity. Class IIb gave less weight to financial advantages than did Class I but it was the members of Class IIa, those dependent on both activities for income, and entrants who gave this aspect the greatest prominence. The function of the second activity in creating employment so that members of the family could continue to work together and its power to widen their social horizons were appreciated most by those who were the most tied to agriculture, that is to say families on the larger and Class I farms and those with farming as the main activity. The information and interest benefits, on the other hand, were valued more by those for whom farming was

Table 9.6 Perceived benefits of part-time farming by income class and development of farmer's career

Class	Income/ capital	Employment/ social	Information/ interest	Comple-mentarity	Lifestyle	Total
			per cent of responses			
I	41.1	20.6	26.1	10.2	2.0	100.0
IIa	46.1	11.9	23.4	9.7	8.9	100.0
IIb	38.7	10.6	28.5	8.7	13.5	100.0 ***
Farmer's main occupation						
Always farming	44.7	20.4	23.8	9.1	2.0	100.0
Entrant	47.7	17.8	21.6	8.0	4.9	100.0
Leaver	40.5	11.1	27.8	10.3	10.3	100.0
Never farming	31.9	6.0	33.0	12.1	17.0	100.0 ***
All responses	41.9	15.6	25.9	9.7	6.9	100.0

(*Source*: 1984 farm survey, sample results)

subsidiary. Attractions of the farming lifestyle were clearly most important where farming was a secondary activity and source of income; comments about the farming lifestyle accounted for nearly 14 per cent of all benefits noted by members of Class IIb but only 2 per cent for those in Class I. Rural retreaters in New South Wales were similarly motivated by a desire to improve their quality of life, expressed in a need for space, seclusion, privacy, recreation, leisure and an attractive environment. Income, tax and speculative ambitions were far less important reasons for acquiring a rural retreat (McQuin 1978:41).

The worst drawbacks of part-time farming were stress, pressures on family life and not having enough time for farm work, as the following quotations show.

Stress

'Always under pressure – too many phone calls – heavy workload – always wanted by three people at once – difficult to keep the activities separate – complicated bookwork – conflict of interests – divided loyalties – forgetting that farming is the main thing.'

Problems for family life

'We never go out as a family from one Christmas to the next – tied to the farm – husband never at home – he hardly ever sees the baby – wife never knows where husband is – wife has to deal with everything when husband is working far away – has to handle calvings – impossible to establish a normal household routine – lateness for meals – lonely on the farm during the day – wife not here to answer the phone – getting your own dinner – children have to fend for themselves – they resent mother being so busy.'

Problems for farming

'Other work has to come first – I must go when the phone rings – I am not always on the spot when problems arise – animals neglected – heavy lambing losses – high vet bills – can't go to cattle markets – can't buy or sell at the optimum time – haymaking is a problem – no time to keep the place tidy – bookkeeping falls behind when wife is working – it slows down progress on a small farm.'

Problems with other job

'Employers disapprove of me having the farm, they think I shouldn't have time for both – tied to customers so lose independence – farm shop attracts thieves at night – heavy lorries cause wear and tear on farm roads – high repair costs for machinery – combining two jobs adds to travelling and administration – transport problems with just the van and a bike between us – visitors can be a nuisance – an invasion of privacy – get under your feet round the farm – disturb the cows.'

Significant differences appeared in the way the three income classes answered the question (Table 9.7). Stress caused by trying to do two jobs, easily the worst drawback in all groups, was given most weight where reliance on farm income was greatest. Difficulties arising on account of the second job such as the additional travelling, invasion of privacy and, in reply to another question, constraints on developing another enterprise on the farm, were also mentioned most frequently by members of Class I. Difficulties in running the farm, on the other hand, were of most concern to part-time farmers in Class IIb who would almost certainly have to give priority to the other job. Class IIb members also laid more emphasis than the rest on the conflict between work and family life which is understandable given the high value which this group places on quality of life.

151

Table 9.7 Perceived drawbacks of part-time farming by income class

Nature of problem	I	IIa	IIb	All replies
		per cent of replies		
Stress	45.9	45.2	38.4	44.0
Other job	20.2	11.4	8.4	14.5
Family life	25.6	25.9	29.5	26.6
Running the farm	8.3	17.5	23.7	14.9
All replies	100.0	100.0	100.0	100.0 ***

(*Source*: 1984 farm survey, sample results)

PREFERRED ACTIVITY

When asked 'If you were completely free to choose, what kind of activity would you and your family prefer?', almost exactly half the respondents in the pilot and main samples voted for full-time farming, rather fewer for combining farming with another job. A small minority had other plans which included giving up farming altogether, retiring or switching to a different non-farm activity (Table 9.8).

Table 9.8 Preferred activity of part-time farmers

Preferred activity	Estimated numbers	Per cent	Per cent in pilot study
Farming only	26 410 a	50.5	49.4
Farming and other job	22 554 a	43.1	30.5
Other replies	3 380 c	6.4	5.1
No reply	–	–	15.0
All replies	52 344	100.0	100.0

(*Source*: 1984 farm survey, raised results and pilot study)

Although full-time farming was the first choice of a majority, by no means all part-time farmers feel themselves to be frustrated full-timers. Some of those interviewed admitted quite candidly that while farming was enjoyable as a spare-time activity, a good complement or an anti-dote to the main job, to farm full time would be worrying, physically exhausting or even boring. Combining a physically challenging activity like farming with a mentally demanding desk job made for a healthy and 'whole' person. One farmer felt that his self-respect depended on having some creative manual activity. Others derived satisfaction from having several irons in the fire. As one fruitgrower-cum-management consultant put it, 'When you have been slogging round in the mud for days on end, it is very enjoyable to leave off your wellingtons one day a week and go up to London to work in a centrally heated office where they call you "Sir".'

Full-time farming was the preferred activity for a majority of those who had started their careers on the land including the leavers, for those working on other farms and for Class I families (the last relationship being significant only in the pilot study). Part-time farming was preferred by a majority of entrants and those never farming as the main activity and by those involved in off-farm work and home businesses.

Since most of those who answered the question were themselves part-time farmers, it may be inferred that those coming into agriculture from non-farm occupations were on the whole more satisfied with part-time farming than those taking the other route out of full-time farming. Assuming that people will tend to profess satisfaction with situations for which they feel responsible and be more likely to complain if they feel they had no choice, it seems to follow that entry into part-time farming from a non-farm occupation is more likely to be perceived as an act of choice while the move from full-time farming is more often made under duress. Once again, however, it was the occupiers of the largest farms who expressed the most positive attitude towards part-time farming; 56 per cent of occupiers in band 4 in the pilot study expressed a preference for part-time farming as against only 31 per cent for the sample as a whole. This supports the impression that part-time farming on holdings which are large and potentially viable is an expression of choice.

SYNTHESIS

Earlier chapters have described 'ideal types' of part-time farming household in terms of the nature of other occupations, the main source of income, the size, type and development of the farm business, the farmer's background, entry to the holding and plans for succession. The present chapter has added a new dimension, exploring farmers' values and attitudes towards part-time farming. Once again it is possible to identify two ideal types, in this case representing contrasting approaches to the farming occupation.

At one pole are those who are strongly oriented to farming as a business, who would probably identify with the interests of full-time commercial farming. This group is well represented among the larger, Class I farms where farming has always been the main activity. Farmers in this group are likely to rate job satisfaction in farming higher than living in the countryside. They are keen to make the best possible income from farming so other objectives which might possibly conflict, such as nature conservation on the farm, may have to take second place. While part-time farmers who are committed to these goals would probably choose to farm full time if the opportunity arose, they recognise a number of advantages in having a second activity. Besides the obvious financial advantages they value the additional employment for other members of the family and the widening of their social horizons. As Wibberley (1977:128) has pointed out, one of the great strengths of part-time farming is its diversity and the choices it offers. Farmers of this persuasion suffer from stress in trying to combine another job with the running of a farm and possibly from frustration when prevented from developing other enterprises on the farm. Their strong farming orientation is well illustrated in their response to the idea of a drop in farm incomes. Their immediate reaction would be to try to improve farm performance by increasing output, raising productivity or switching to a more profitable farming system.

The other ideal type finds farming more attractive as a way of life than as a way of making a living. Members of this group might identify more readily with the rural non-farm population than with the interests of large-scale commercial agriculture. They are well represented on the smaller part-time holdings and in Class II, particularly IIb. Numerically they may be the stronger group though not so influential within the farming industry. Country living is typically rated higher than job satisfaction in the farming occupation. Farming is valued as a new interest, an activity which all the family can share. Perhaps for this reason, pressures of work which encroach on family life and leisure time are regarded more seriously than by the first group. Making the highest possible income from the farm is typically subordinated to other goals such as capital appreciation and nature conservation. The security of owning land and a house may be of particular value to them (Wibberley 1977:124–5). If the profitability of farming is threatened, their first reaction might be to do nothing but if the drain on resources grows too heavy, these occupiers might decide to give up farming altogether. For preference, however, they would continue to combine the two occupations.

Chapter
10

Conclusions

Part-time farming is much more widespread in Britain than is commonly realised. According to the 1983 EC Farm Structure Survey over 30 per cent of main agricultural holdings in England and Wales were run on a part-time basis in the sense that the occupier and/or spouse had another paid job besides working on the holding. Yet although the idea that nearly one-third of the farms in England and Wales are part-time farms may come as a surprise to some, this could be regarded as a minimum figure. The definition of part-time farming excludes company farms and minor holdings where, for different reasons, the incidence of other gainful activities is likely to be high. It only takes into consideration the activities of the principal farmer and spouse, ignoring occupations of junior partners and their spouses and other members of the farm household. It is confined to dual-job holding by individuals, leaving out of account households in which some members work exclusively on and some exclusively off the farm.

For practical purposes it is necessary to draw boundaries. The definition adopted for the 1983 Structure Survey, which determined the framework for the present study, was perfectly adequate for the task in hand. It concentrated attention on the most clear-cut cases of part-time farming, enabling survey resources to be used to good effect. Lowering the size threshold to include minor holdings or taking the farm household rather than the individual occupier as the unit of analysis would undoubtedly have brought more holdings within the definition but it would also have blunted the concept since many of those drawn in would have had negligible farm output or minimal off-farm earnings.

In a sense any boundary could be regarded as arbitrary. There are probably very few farm households entirely without other sources of earned income. While the present study focuses on those with the most significant and acknowledged other activities, these should perhaps be regarded as a subset of the farming population rather than a separate population altogether. The emphasis ought to be on the *activity* of combining another gainful occupation with farming rather than on any particular, defined group of farmers which happens to engage in this activity to a greater degree than the rest.

The population of part-time farmers is in any case so heterogeneous, it is difficult to speak of them as a group in any but the most general terms. This study has pointed to contrasts in the nature of other activities and in the relative dependence on farming and other income sources, relating these differences to features of the farmer's background and previous experience and his route into farming. The effects of these differences may be traced in the goals, values and attitudes of the farmers themselves and in the scale, type and complexity of their farming systems.

Two contrasting types of part-time farming family have been depicted, the one more oriented to farming as a business and an occupation, the other to a farming lifestyle. The first group can be identified broadly with Class I and with larger holdings, with a farming background and farming always being the main activity. This type is well represented in East Anglia and the north of England. The opposite tendencies predominate among families on the smallest holdings where there is another main income source; that is to say the other occupation probably came first chronologically, the holding was most likely purchased, possibly within the last ten years and will probably not be handed on to the next generation. Families of this type, often attracted to farm ownership by motives of investment, residence and amenity, are particularly numerous in the south of England and also in the heavily populated north-west. It has to be remembered, however, that these are ideal types, set up to aid understanding but not necessarily corresponding to actual cases. Some families do not fit easily into either camp.

Households in which farming plays a secondary role are in the majority and account for about one-fifth of the entire farming population of England and Wales. The predominance of the Class II type of part-time farming household is upheld whether comparison is made in terms of use of the farmer's time, what each person regards as the main activity or contributions to total household income. Following trends in other developed countries, the farm population in England and Wales as a whole is likely to become increasingly dependent on other sources of income. Pointers to this trend are that over the past forty years the Class II type of part-time farming has been increasing relative to Class I and full-time farming, that Class II predominates among more recent entrants to agriculture and that younger part-time farmers are more likely than older ones to regard the other job as the main activity. This has important implications for agricultural policy.

POLICY IMPLICATIONS OF PART-TIME FARMING

Chapter 1 suggested that part-time farming was 'in tune with the times'. It promises to keep more families on the land by supplementing their incomes from farming, thereby helping to maintain rural communities and it may also be seen as a means of safeguarding the natural environment. The validity of these suggestions can now be assessed in the light of the evidence presented in the previous eight chapters.

If two-thirds of part-time farming households habitually earn more from other sources than from farming, it is reasonable to suppose that most of them would be unable to remain on their farms without those other occupations. It seems likely, too, that many of the families which depend mainly on the income from farming, would not be able to carry on without a supplementary income source. Upwards of 40 000 families, at a rough guess, are being enabled to remain on the land by virtue of other sources of earned income.

Although part-time farming alleviates the problem of low incomes in agriculture, it does not remove it completely. The farm survey estimated that about 10 per cent of part-time farming households, about 5000 families, had made less than £4000 from farming and other activities combined in the previous financial year. These families appeared to be concentrated in the south and west of England, with a third of them in the south-west region alone. Often the second activity was a farm-based enterprise. Four-fifths of the low income families were in Class I, mainly dependent on farming for their living. Whether their farm incomes were chronically low or only unstable, whether low earnings were supplemented by pensions or investment income or mitigated by low living costs and whether there were obstacles preventing these families from improving their income position, could not be determined with the information available. There were indications, however, that the most serious income problems were associated with holdings which were too small to yield an adequate income from farming alone yet too large to allow the farmer to take another full-time job. This suggests there may be a need for ex-full-time farmers taking other jobs to reorganise their farms along more extensive, labour-saving lines.

The notion of 'maintaining the fabric of rural society', to which the Perspectives Green Paper referred several times, is nowhere clearly defined. At the very least it must mean maintaining numbers of rural dwellers. In this direction part-time farming could be said to have some success since it keeps families on farms, if not actually creating much additional employment. (Indications from the farm survey were that most of those employed by part-time farmers worked on their farms.) On the other hand it might be argued that while part-time farming is strongly established in the more prosperous, heavily populated south of England, it appears to be less successful in northern England and Wales where threats of rural depopulation are more real.

While part-time farming may help to maintain numbers, it is unlikely to bring *stability* to rural areas. In the normal course of events, larger full-time farm businesses are handed down from father to son but smaller and part-time farms tend to change hands more rapidly and not to remain within the family. Among the Class II part-time farmers in the present study only about a third had succession in mind. Over 40 per cent of those who were farming on a part-time basis in 1984 had been in occupation of their present holdings for less than 10 years. Rapid turnover of families on smaller holdings is likely to have a disruptive influence on rural communities. Besides this, the families which are enabled to continue living on small farms by virtue of other occupations may have little in common with those who were there before. Nearly half the part-time farmers in the country came into agriculture from other walks of life and, for nearly a third of them, farming has never been more than a sideline. Recent entrants to part-time farming and occupiers of the smallest holdings include a high proportion of those from other backgrounds for whom farming has never been the main source of income and employment. Often these newcomers have different value systems, expectations and priorities from the full-time farmers they replace. It follows that part-time farming will be unlikely to preserve the rural social structure unchanged. Whether it is therefore to be judged as beneficial or harmful to rural society must remain a subjective question. Some would view any change in the composition of rural society as a threat while others recognise that living communities, like living organisms, must continually develop and adapt to changing circumstances if they are to survive.

The goal of protecting the rural environment is attracting a growing amount of support in Britain. The type of farming favoured by the bulk of part-time farmers is likely to be compatible with this goal. Part-time farms in general carry fewer enterprises than full-time farms, often specialising in grazing cattle, sheep or horses. On the whole there is little propensity to expand the area of the holding, intensify

production or make capital improvements, changes which may be seen
as a threat to the natural environment. The Class II type of part-time
farmer, less dependent on farming for a living and therefore less likely
to be trapped on the technological treadmill, exemplifies all these
traits in a more extreme form. There was some evidence from the pilot
study that Class II part-time farmers and those from non-farm backgrounds were more strongly in favour of nature conservation than the
rest and that they had taken more positive steps to introduce conservation practices on their own farms. The environmentalist should
therefore welcome the probable expansion of the Class II type of
part-time farming although he should also remember that while Class
II part-time farms currently account for about two-thirds of total
numbers, they only occupy about 40 per cent of the total area in part-
time holdings. The objectives and farming practices of the Class I
group controlling 60 per cent of the land are probably closer to those
of full-time commercial farmers.

Turning from the social and environmental goals of agricultural
policy to the economic, it is difficult to weigh up the pros and cons
of part-time farming at a time when the long-term objectives of the
industry are so unclear. An emphasis on enterprises like beef and
sheep with fairly low levels of capital investment, low labour inputs
and low output per hectare must mean that the amount of food
produced by part-time farms is below its full potential. Part-time farms
as a whole are not characterised by rapid rates of expansion or capital
investment either. If the goal of agricultural policy were to maximise
production from the land, as it was during the Second World War,
part-time farming would obviously have to be discouraged. If the goal
is to maximise efficiency or productivity, the case against part-time
farming is not proven. The present study produced little evidence that
part-time farms in general, and supplementary-income farms in
particular, make less efficient use of land than main-living farms; if
anything the evidence points the other way. With respect to labour
productivity, part-time farming certainly has the power to counteract
the problem of under employment of farmer and wife's labour, which
is one of the main causes of low productivity on the smaller farm.

At the present time the goals of maintaining food supplies and
improving efficiency are being overshadowed by the problems of
accumulating surpluses and the need to achieve market balance. Part-
time farming must score on this count. The combination of beef or
sheep and another occupation offers an alternative to milk production
on the small family-worked farm. The arable farmer with another business is not under such pressure to push up yields and enlarge his
cereal acreage, with beneficial consequences for the grain mountain
and, incidentally, for the environment. Here once again the distinction between Class I and Class II part-time farming should be kept

in mind. Under the threat of falling farm incomes members of Class I would be more inclined to try to improve farm performance, behaving much like full-time farmers. By contrast the Class II type of part-time farmer might not respond at all if farm income was not an important consideration for him. Lower prices for cereals, beef or sheepmeat might therefore elicit different responses from Class I and Class II part-time farmers.

In broad terms, then, part-time farming appears to be compatible with the aims of keeping families on the land, protecting their incomes and safeguarding the farmed landscape without adding to surpluses or increasing the burden on the taxpayer. It is the smaller, Class II part-time farms which seem better placed to achieve the production, environmental and social goals of agricultural policy as it is evolving, although not perhaps without some cost in terms of disrupting rural communities. Yet farms of this type receive very little encouragement from the state. According to the Perspectives Green Paper the new EC structures policy is intended to supply aid to a much wider range of farmers, particularly those in the lower income bracket. The farm surveys found, nevertheless, that part-time farmers on smaller holdings are less likely than those on larger farms to invest in the holding or to receive grant aid for improvements and they are more likely to have their requests for aid turned down. The small and Class II part-time farm does not qualify for aid under the Agricultural Improvement Regulations and is not eligible for the beef-cow subsidy. The pilot study indicated that the information and advisory needs of small-scale part-time farmers were not being met either. The only specific encouragement for part-time farming from the state is for tourism and craft enterprises in Less Favoured Areas but, as this study has shown, such farm-based activities account for a small proportion of the jobs of part-time farming families.

There would seem to be considerable scope for removing discrimination against part-time farming in Britain by broadening the basis of eligibility for capital grants. A neutral stance might be the best approach to aim for. Positive discrimination in favour of part-time farming would be liable to raise more problems than it solved. It might for example force up the price of smaller properties, with socially undesirable consequences. A more realistic approach might be to improve the part-time farmer's access to information, advice and training. In this connection it is necessary to establish first of all how many part-time farmers are 'leavers' from a full-time farming background who are attempting to diversify into other activities and how many are 'entrants' trying to secure a niche in farming. The training and advisory needs of the two groups are obviously quite different.

Various initiatives which have been observed in Britain and abroad give some idea of practical steps which might be taken to assist the small and part-time farmer. An agricultural college in Ontario, for instance, offers a 'Night School Program for Novice Farmers' (Hutchinson 1976). In similar vein a College of Further Education in Yorkshire has successfully launched courses for smallholders and part-time farmers in such subjects as basic animal husbandry and practical farm bookkeeping. In New South Wales the Department of Agriculture, overwhelmed by requests for advice from 'rural re-treaters', produced a handbook on 'Small Area Farming'. A small farm group in west Wales caters for the needs of part-time farmers with a programme of lectures and farm walks and produces a very practical newsletter which contains not only topical technical advice but also information about discount buying, an 'Exchange and Mart' section and a register of skills which members are willing to offer for payment, consultation or exchange.

IMPLICATIONS FOR THE FAMILY

Chapter 3 argued the case for a family or household approach to the study of part-time farming. Farms are not usually operated by farmers on their own but involve the labour and cooperation of other members of the family. Wives in particular are likely to be drawn into a variety of farm tasks and decision-making activities. Where the farmer has another occupation the rest of the family may have to shoulder extra responsibilities on the farm or he may concentrate on the farming side while other family members supplement the household income from other sources.

The farm survey did not, in fact, produce much evidence of family members other than the farmer and spouse being involved in farm work or in other gainful occupations. One quarter of all part-time farming households were estimated to have more than two breadwinners, the proportion rising to one-third on the largest holdings. This may have been partly due to the way the sample was drawn since households in which members other than farmer or spouse had other paid jobs were not sampled. (Following the convention of the agricultural census, the survey excluded any consideration of farm work by children still in full-time education. The degree to which part-time farming families rely on the unpaid labour of children is therefore not known but might be significant.) It was in fact on the largest farms and those where the farmer himself spent most time working that the labour contribution of other family members was greatest. Employment of non-family labour, too, was greatest on the largest farms. This seems to suggest that the higher labour requirements of larger farms outweigh any effect of labour substitution for absent farmers on smaller holdings.

Another argument for making the farm household rather than the individual occupier the unit of analysis is that the household is the consumption unit, the social group involved in making a living. The farm survey therefore tried to ascertain whether all household earnings were pooled. From the evidence available it appeared that in only about half the households where there were members other than the farmer and spouse earning did those members contribute to the family budget. Usually it was a case of sons and daughters making a modest contribution for their keep. In few cases the income provided by other family members was sufficient to push total household earnings into a higher income bracket or swing the balance from farming to another main source of income. The information obtained was not felt to be wholly satisfactory, however, and the topic would repay more careful study.

The fact that the farm family is not a constant unit but variable in its income needs and labour resources over the course of the family cycle is another good reason for making the family the unit of analysis. Quite striking differences were revealed by the farm survey in household composition between the regions of England and Wales. Young families were most characteristic of northern England and Wales, families in the middle stage of development with children working were most characteristic of north-west England, Yorkshire/Humberside and the East Midlands and families in the 'empty-nest' stage of East Anglia. Three generation households were most common in the West Midlands and Wales while the east and south of England had the most incomplete families. These differences were reflected in the size and composition of the labour force and in succession plans. How the differences arise is not clear, although Chapter 3 speculated on the question. It is not known either whether differences in household composition are a cause or an effect of part-time farming, nor even whether the pattern observed is a feature of part-time farming alone or applies to farm families in general.

Although the case was made for an all-embracing household approach to the study of part-time farming, the main survey and the pilot were necessarily constrained by the samples provided, which in turn depended upon the questions asked in the 1980 and 1983 LIIs. There the emphasis was on dual-job holding by farmers and spouses individually and inevitably these roles have featured most prominently in the present study. Farm households with a 'looser' role structure, where for instance the farmer works exclusively on the farm and his wife or son exclusively elsewhere, can equally be regarded as part-time farming households but they are under-represented here.

A good deal of information is accumulating on the roles of wives in part-time farming. Over 60 per cent of part-time farmers had received some assistance from their spouses on the farm in the preceding year. On average, wives who work on part-time farms put in sixteen hours a week, little short of the hours recorded for working wives on full-time farms. Whereas the amount of farm work the farmer does is closely related to farm size and the level of reliance on farm income, the wife's contribution appears to be determined more by family and cultural values. Wives make their greatest impact in the early stage of the family cycle despite having young children at home, and they are more likely to help on the farm in northern England than in the south.

Two of the most striking discoveries from the Labour Input Inquiries concerned the activities of spouses. One was that farmers with other jobs were three times as likely as full-time farmers to have spouses with other jobs. This relationship, which appeared to be independent of farm size, was confirmed by two separate studies in the United States. The other surprising result was the apparent rapid increase in dual-job holding by farmers' spouses between the two Labour Input Inquiries; from under 5 per cent of all holdings in 1979/80 to nearly 11 per cent in 1983. A tentative explanation was offered along the lines that part-time farmers would be likely to hold more liberal views than full-time farmers about women's work and so would be more likely to record their wives' gainful activities on and off the farm in the LII. This does not explain why similar results were obtained in the United States and the whole issue of wives' involvement in the farm-household economy deserves a more thorough investigation.

Results of the farm surveys support the suggestion that on small-holdings farmers and their wives need second jobs in order to make ends meet but on larger farms having another occupation is rather an expression of choice. For wives on larger farms in particular, having another job may be a means of pursuing a vocation, of gaining recognition, of achieving an identity apart from that of housewife and mother. Without any prompting a number of farmers mentioned the enjoyment and stimulus which their wives gained from having careers of their own off the farm as one of the advantages of part-time farming, a benefit which rubbed off on to other members of the family too. On larger farms it is more usual for the farmer's wife alone to have another paid job and often this will be a professional occupation off the farm, unrelated to agriculture such as nursing or teaching. More wives than farmers are qualified for non-farm occupations but even so the 'top' professional posts like lawyer and doctor are more likely to be held by men.

Finally, what are the implications of part-time farming for farmers themselves? Throughout this study the emphasis has been on differences between various categories of part-time farmers; for example, between those with farming as a major and minor activity or as the main and subsidiary source of income, between those from farm and non-farm backgrounds, and so on. If this diverse collection of individuals shares any characteristic in common, it must be that they are highly motivated and very busy people.

One penalty for having two occupations is the long hours of work. This holds true whether the farmer runs a full-time farm business with another activity as a sideline or has another major occupation and farms in his spare time. Most part-time farmers are solely responsible for the day-to-day running of their holdings and tackle every kind of job that needs to be done, with or without help. The pilot study estimated that their average labour input on the holding amounted to 30 hours a week throughout the year. On top of this, about a third of the part-time farmers with off-farm jobs had to make journeys of more than ten miles each way. All this adds up to a very full schedule for many part-time farmers. It was hardly surprising then, that many felt themselves to be continually under pressure, torn by conflicting loyalties, burdened by a heavy workload. The farm might have to be neglected for the sake of the second job which, being the main source of income in two cases out of three, could not be put in jeopardy. Family life and leisure were frequently sacrificed in the interests of both. Almost half of all the drawbacks of part-time farming which were mentioned by respondents in the farm survey related to stress.

Despite these pressures, part-time farmers as a whole find more advantages than disadvantages in their situation. Although their reasons for combining another job with farming are extremely varied, ranging from stark economic necessity to the desire to savour a farming lifestyle, few would willingly exchange farming for any other activity. Even the threat of a severe drop in farm income would not deter many of them. Four out of five rated job satisfaction in the farming occupation as very important to them personally. If they were completely free to choose what they would do, only a tiny minority would prefer to do something else; the great majority would carry on farming.

Glossary of terms

Classification of occupations
All gainful activities of farm-household members other than farm work
on the holding are divided into work taking place on and off the
holding. Work taking place on the holding is then divided into *farm-
based enterprises* (providing accommodation, catering for recreational
and sporting interests, adding value to farm products) and *home businesses* (home workshop, home agency). A farm base is felt to be essential to the first but not the second. Work taking place off the holding
is subdivided into *work on other farms* (management, agricultural
contracting, wage work) and *off-farm work* (business, professions,
service and manual occupations excluding farm work).

Development of farmer's career
Farmers are classified according to the way their careers have developed into:

* *always farming*, where farming was the first main occupation after
  completing full-time education and National Service and is the
  main occupation now;
* *leaver*, where farming was the first main occupation but is no longer
  the main occupation;
* *entrant*, where farming was not the first but is now the farmer's
  main occupation;
* *never farming*, where farming was not the first main occupation and
  is not the main occupation now.

Dual-job holder
A person who combines another paid job with farm work on the holding.

ESU (European Size Unit)[1]
A measure of farm business size. One ESU equals 1000 European Units of Account of Standard Gross Margin at average 1972/4 values.

Farm household
All persons normally living under the same roof as the farmer and sharing common housekeeping. Children away at boarding school or college are excluded but non-related persons living in the household such as living-in students and resident domestic help are included.

Farm types[1]
Farms are classified by MAFF on the basis of Standard Gross Margins per unit of crop area and per head of livestock. This is the classification used to analyse data from the Labour Input Inquiry (see Table 7.4).

Income classification
Part-time farming households are classified on the basis of the latest available information on total household earned income into:

- *Class I* in which 50 per cent of more of total household earned income is from farming the holding;
- *Class II* in which less than 50 per cent of total household income is earned from farming the holding. This group is subdivided into:
- *Class IIa* with a positive income from farming in the latest year; and
- *Class IIb* in which farming the holding made no net contribution to total household earnings in the latest financial year.

Labour efficiency index
The ratio of the amount of labour available on the holding in a given year to the standard labour requirement of the holding for the same period. The ratio is expressed as days available per 100 smd theoretically required. Lower values indicate a more efficient use of labour.

LII (Labour Input Inquiry)
Postal surveys of stratified random samples of agricultural holdings conducted by MAFF in 1980 and 1983 as part of the 1979/80 and 1983 EC Farm Structure Surveys.

Minor holding[1]

A holding which satisfies all the following conditions:

- total area of holding less than 6 hectares;
- no regular whole-time farmer or worker on the holding;
- annual labour requirement of less than 100 smd;
- glasshouse area less than 100 sq. m;
- the occupier does not farm another holding.

Census returns for minor holdings (formerly statistically insignificant holdings) are only made every four or five years. All other agricultural holdings (main holdings, formerly statistically significant holdings) are surveyed every year.

Natural person

A person running a farm business as sole occupier or partner with unlimited liability. Those running farms as limited companies, limited partnerships and 'other kinds of occupiers' are excluded.

OECD

Organisation for Economic Cooperation and Development.

Part-time farming

The combination of farming with other paid work.

Part-time farming family/household

A family or household whose members combine other paid work with farming.

Part-time farm/holding

A farm or agricultural holding run by a part-time farming family or household.

Part-time farmer

Operator of a part-time farm.

SGM (standard gross margin)[1]

A financial measure used to classify farms by size and type. It is based on the concept of the gross margin which, for any enterprise, is given by enterprise output less variable costs. Standards have been calculated for the English regions and for Wales, Scotland and Northern Ireland for the period 1978/80. The total SGM for a farm is the sum of SGMs for its various enterprises.

Size bands

The sample of holdings drawn for the 1984 farm survey was stratified by size of business into four bands which were intended to illustrate the following situations:

1. *Main holdings below 100 smd*, judged to have some farming activity but small enough to be managed as spare-time enterprises;
2. *Holdings of 100 to 249 smd*, judged too small to provide full-time employment for one person or an adequate income for a family but probably too large for spare-time working;
3. *Holdings of 250 to 499 smd* which should generate enough work to keep one person fully occupied but likely to be marginal in terms of family income needs;
4. *Holdings of 500 smd and over*, full-time commercial holdings which should be capable of employing at least two people full time and yielding an adequate income for a family.

SMD (standard man day)[1]
A measure of farm business size. A standard man day represents 8 hours of productive work by an adult worker under average conditions.

---

[1] For further details see MAFF publications such as *Farm Incomes in the United Kingdom 1986*, HMSO.

Statistical tests

CONFIDENCE LIMITS

Where results of the 1984 farm survey have been raised to give estimates for the whole population, the letters a, b and c denote confidence limits for the raised estimate. The 95 per cent confidence limits for the estimates are:

a within 10 per cent of the estimate;

b within 20 per cent of the estimate;

c within 33 per cent of the estimate.

See, for instance, Table 3.3 where the figure a appears against the estimate of 22 130 part-time farming families in the early stage of the family cycle. This implies that in 95 cases out of 100 one would be correct in assuming that the true number of part-time farming families in the population in the early stage lay between 19 917 and 24 343.

TEST OF ASSOCIATION

In a number of tables the strength of association between two variables has been tested using the statistic Chi square (see, for example, Tables 3.4, 4.2, 5.3). Asterisks indicate that the association is significant at or beyond   * the 10 per cent level of probability;

** the 5 per cent level;

*** the 1 per cent level.

The symbol 'ns' means that the association is not significant at the 10 per cent level while no symbol implies that no test of significance has been carried out.

In Table 3.4 the symbol *** indicates that if there were no real association between standard region and stage in the family cycle, an association as strong as the one observed in the sample could only occur by chance once in a hundred cases. In other words one can feel confident that the association suggested by the survey data reflects a real association in the population at large and not just a freak of sampling.

References

Agriculture EDC 1972 *Agricultural manpower in England and Wales.* HMSO

Agriculture EDC 1973 *Farm productivity. A report on factors affecting productivity at the farm level.* HMSO

Ahearn M, Johnson J, Strickland R 1985 The distribution of income and wealth of farm operator households. *American Journal of Agricultural Economics* 67(5):1087–94

Alden J, Spooner R 1981 *An analysis of second jobs in the European Community.* University of Wales Institute of Science and Technology, Department of Town Planning (Papers in planning research 35)

Arkleton Trust 1985 *Part-time farming in the rural development of industrialized countries.* The Arkleton Trust

Ashton J, Cracknell B E 1961 Agricultural holdings and farm business structure in England and Wales. *Journal of Agricultural Economics* xiv(4):472–500

Bergmann D, Laurent C 1977 Research needs and priorities. In Gasson R (ed.) *The place of part-time farming in rural and regional development.* Wye College Centre for European Agricultural Studies, pp. 5–15

Blair A M 1978 Spatial effects of urban influences on agriculture in Essex 1960–1974. Unpublished PhD thesis, University College London Department of Geography

Board of Agriculture and Fisheries 1907 *Agricultural Statistics 1907.* HMSO

Bolin O, Persson L O 1978 Forecasting changes in the agricultural structure: three system simulation models. *European Review of Agricultural Economics* 4(3):187–214

Bollman R D 1979 *Off-farm work by farmers.* Statistics Canada, Ottawa

Bollman R D, Steeves A D 1980 *The stocks and flows of Canadian census-farm operators over the period 1966–1976.* Paper presented to 5th World Congress for Rural Sociology, Mexico City

Bollman R D 1982 Part-time farming in Canada: issues and non-issues. *GeoJournal* 6(4):313–22

Bouquet M 1985 *Family, servants and visitors. The farm household in nineteenth and twentieth century Devon.* Geo Books

Britton D K, Hill B 1975 *Size and efficiency in farming.* Saxon House

Brun A 1977 Case studies of part time farming in less favoured areas. In Gasson R (ed.) *The place of part-time farming in rural and regional development.* Wye College Centre for European Agricultural Studies, pp. 55–69

Bull C J, Wibberley G P 1976 *Farm based recreation in S E England.* Wye College (Studies in rural land use 12)

Bunce M 1976 The contribution of the part-time farmer to the rural economy. In Fuller A M, Mage J A (eds) *Part-time farming: problem or resource in rural development.* Geo Abstracts, pp 249–57

Butler J B 1958 *The small farms of industrial Yorkshire.* University of Leeds Department of Agriculture, Economics Section

Buttel F H 1982 The political economy of part-time farming. *GeoJournal* 6(4):293–300

Buttel F H, Gillespie G W Jr 1984 The sexual division of farm household labor: an exploratory study of the structure of on-farm and off-farm labor allocation among farm men and women. *Rural Sociology* 49(2):183–209

Carlin T A, Ghelfi L M 1979 Off-farm employment and the farm sector. In *Structure issues of American agriculture.* US Government Printing Office, Washington DC, pp. 270–3

Cavazzani A 1976 Social determinants of part-time farming in a marginal region of Italy. In Fuller A M, Mage J A (eds) *Part-time farming: problem or resource in rural development.* Geo Abstracts, pp. 101–13

Cavazzani A, Fuller A M 1982 International perspectives on part-time farming: a review. *GeoJournal* 6(4):383–9

Cawley M 1983 Part time farming in rural development: evidence from western Ireland. *Sociologia Ruralis* xxiii(1):63–75

Centre for European Agricultural Studies 1977 *Part-time farming: its nature and implications. A workshop report.* Wye College Centre for European Agricultural Studies

Christodoulou D 1982 Part-time farming in the developing world: a case of Hobson's choice or the privilege of half a loaf. *GeoJournal* 6(4):373–80

Cloke P J 1977 An index of rurality for England and Wales. *Regional Studies* 11:31–46

Commission of the European Communities 1980 *The agricultural situation in the Community: 1979 report.* Commission of the European Communities, Brussels/Luxembourg

Commission of the European Communities 1985 *Perspectives for the Common Agricultural Policy. The green paper of the Commission.* Commission of the European Communities, Brussels

Coughenour C M, Christenson J A 1981 *Farm structure, social class, and farmers' policy perspectives.* University of Kentucky College of Agriculture, Department of Sociology, Agriculture Experiment Station

Coughenour C M, Swanson L 1983 Work statuses and occupations of men and women in farm families and the structure of farms. *Rural Sociology* 48:23–43

Country Landowners' Association 1980 *Report of the working party on employment in rural areas.* Country Landowners' Association

Craps R 1977 Problems of integrating policies. In Gasson R (ed.) *The place of part-time farming in rural and regional development.* Wye College Centre for European Agricultural Studies, pp. 16–20

Curry J 1972 Effects of non-farm employment in rural areas. *Farm and Food Research* 3(1):4–7

Davies E T 1969 *Tourism and the Cornish farmer.* University of Exeter Department of Economics (Report 173)

Davies E T 1971 *Farm tourism in Cornwall and Devon: some economic and physical considerations.* University of Exeter Agricultural Economics Unit (Report 184)

Davies E T 1973 *Tourism on Devon farms: a physical and economic appraisal.* University of Exeter Agricultural Economics Unit (Report 188)

Deseran F A 1984 Farm and rural nonfarm youth in the labor force: some observations. In Schwarzweller H K (ed.) *Focus on Agriculture.* JAI Press, Greenwich, Connecticut, pp. 105–33 (Research in rural sociology and development volume 1)

Deseran F A 1985 Off-farm employment and social networks of Louisiana farm couples. *Sociologia Ruralis* xxv(2):174–88

Deseran F A (forthcoming) Part-time farming and commuting:

determinants of distance to off-farm work for Louisiana farm couples. In Falk W, Lyson T (eds) *Research in rural sociology and development: a research annual*. JAI Press, Greenwich, Connecticut

Dunn J M 1969 Some features of small full-time and large part-time farms in Scotland. *Scottish Agricultural Economics* xix:205–20

Dunn J M 1975 Some aspects of the structure of Scottish farming. *Scottish Agricultural Economics* xxv:373–5

Dzierwickla M 1976 Dual occupation in Polish agriculture. In Turowski J, Szwengrub L M (eds) *Rural social change in Poland*. Polish Academy of Science, Warsaw

Edwards C J W 1980 Changing farm size and land occupancy in central Somerset: a note. *Journal of Agricultural Economics* xxxi(2):249–51

Edwards C J W 1982 Land mobility on farms in Northern Ireland. *Journal of Agricultural Economics* xxxiii(1):89–91

Enyedi G 1982 Part-time farming in Hungary. *GeoJournal* 6(4):323–6

Frank W 1983 Part time farming, underemployment and double activity of farmers in the EEC. *Sociologia Ruralis* xxiii(l):20–7

Fuguitt G V 1961 A typology of the part-time farmer. *Rural Sociology* 26(1):39–48

Fuller A M 1976 The problems of part-time farming conceptualised. In Fuller A M, Mage J A (eds) *Part-time farming: problem or resource in rural development*. Geo Abstracts, pp. 38–56

Fuller A M 1983 Part time farming and the farm family: a note for future research. *Sociologia Ruralis* xxiii(1):5–10

Furness G W 1983 The importance, distribution and net incomes of small farm businesses in the UK. In Tranter R B (ed.) *Strategies for family-worked farms in the UK*. University of Reading Centre for Agricultural Strategy, pp. 12–41 (CAS paper 15)

Galloway J I 1975 *The 'persistent' part-time farmer*. Paper submitted for Canadian Association of Geographers' Regional Conference, Carleton University, Ottawa

Gardner T W 1951 *The farms and estates of Oxfordshire*. University of Reading Department of Agricultural Economics (Miscellaneous studies 5)

Gasson R 1966 *The influence of urbanization on farm ownership and practice*. Wye College Department of Agricultural Economics (Studies in rural land use 7)

Gasson R 1967 Some economic characteristics of part-time farming in Britain. *Journal of Agricultural Economics* xviii(1):111–20

Gasson R 1973 Goals and values of farmers. *Journal of Agricultural Economics* xxiv(3):521–38

Gasson R 1980a *The role of women in British agriculture.* Women's Farm and Garden Association

Gasson R 1980b Sex equality is still a long way off. *Farmers Weekly* 10 Oct. 1980

Gasson R 1984 Farm women in Europe: their need for off-farm employment. *Sociologia Ruralis* xxiv(3/4):216–28

Gasson R 1986 Part-time farming: strategy for survival? *Sociologia Ruralis* xxvi(3/4):364–76

Goss K F, Rodefeld R D, Buttel F H 1979 *The political economy of class structure in US agriculture: a theoretical outline.* The Pennsylvania State University Department of Agricultural Economics and Rural Sociology (AE and RS report 144)

Hanf C-H, Müller R A E 1974/5 Multiple job holding and leisure time. *European Review of Agricultural Economics* 2(1):87–93

Harrison A 1965 Some features of farm business structures. *Journal of Agricultural Economics* xvi(3):330–54

Harrison A 1966 *The farms of Buckinghamshire: some features of farm businesses in a county adjoining Greater London.* University of Reading Department of Agricultural Economics (Miscellaneous studies 40)

Harrison A 1967 *Farming change in Buckinghamshire: some features revealed in a study of farm business structure 1961–1963.* University of Reading Department of Agricultural Economics (Miscellaneous studies 43)

Harrison A 1975 *Farmers and farm businesses in England.* University of Reading Department of Agricultural Economics and Management (Miscellaneous study 62)

Hathaway D E, Perkins B E 1968 Occupational mobility and migration from agriculture. In *Rural poverty in the United States.* A report by the President's National Advisory Commission on Rural Poverty, US Government Printing Office, Washington DC, Chapter 13 pp. 185–237

Heath D W 1976 The 1975 E.E.C. Farm Structure Survey. *Journal of Agricultural Economics* xxvii(3):321–30

Heatherington S 1983 Potential effects of part time farming on the household and the rural economy. *Sociologia Ruralis* xxiii(1):85–8

Higgins J 1983 *A study of part-time farmers in the Republic of Ireland.* Economics and Rural Welfare Centre, An Foras Taluntais, Dublin

Hill B 1982 Concepts and measurement of the incomes, wealth and economic well-being of farmers. *Journal of Agricultural Economics* xxxiii(3):311–24

Hill B 1987 Multiple sources of income: implications for family incomes and farm income support. *Journal of Agricultural Economics* xxxviii(2):182–9

Hutchinson G 1976 Educating the novice farmer. In Fuller A M, Mage J A (eds) *Part-time farming: problem or resource in rural development*. Geo Abstracts, pp. 154–62

Jolliffe W 1977 Farming in the rural urban fringe in Britain. In Gasson R (ed) *The place of part-time farming in rural and regional development*. Wye College Centre for European Agricultural Studies, pp. 35–41

Jones C, Rosenfeld R A 1981 *American farm women: findings from a national survey*. National Opinion Research Center, Chicago (NORC report 130)

Kada R 1980 *Part-time family farming. Off-farm employment and farm adjustments in the United States and Japan*. Center for Academic Publications Japan, Tokyo

Kada R 1982a Trends and characteristics of part-time farming in post-war Japan. *GeoJournal* 6(4):367–71

Kada R 1982b Part-time farming in Japan: definition, trends and adjustments. In Krasovec S (ed.) *Part-time farmers and their adjustment to pluriactivity. Part II*. Slovene Academy of Science and Arts, Ljubljana, Yugoslavia, pp. 309–21

Kłodziński M 1983 Part-time farming in Polish agriculture. *Oxford Agrarian Studies* 12:16–33

Krasovec S 1977 Part time farming: implications for income and price policy. In Gasson R (ed.) *The place of part-time farming in rural and regional development*. Wye College Centre for European Agricultural Studies, pp. 82–91

Krasovec S 1983 Farmers' adjustment to pluriactivity. *Sociologia Ruralis* xxiii(1):11–19

Laurent C 1982 Multiple jobholding farmers in agricultural policy. *GeoJournal* 6(4):287–92

Lucey D I F, Kaldor D R 1969 *Rural industrialization: the impact of industrialization on two rural communities in western Ireland*. Geoffrey Chapman

Lyson T A 1984 Pathways into production agriculture: the structuring of farm recruitment in the United States. In Schwarzweller H K (ed.) *Focus on Agriculture*. JAI Press, Greenwich, Connecticut, pp. 79–103 (Research in rural sociology and development volume 1)

MacLean H 1977 Implications of part time farming for less favoured areas: the case of the Highlands and Islands Development Board. In Gasson R (ed.) *The place of part-time farming in rural and regional development*. Wye College Centre for European Agricultural Studies, pp. 46–54

McLeay P 1976 Part-time farming in Britain: a study of statutory smallholdings in south Staffordshire. In Fuller A M, Mage J A (eds) *Part-time farming: problem or resource in rural development*. Geo Abstracts, pp. 83–93

McQuin P 1978 *Rural retreating: a review and an Australian case study*. University of New England Department of Geography

Mage J A 1976 A typology of part-time farming. In Fuller A M, Mage J A (eds) *Part-time farming: problem or resource in rural development*. Geo Abstracts, pp. 6–37

Martens L 1980 Part-time farming in developed countries. *European Review of Agricultural Economics* 7:377–93

Ministry of Agriculture and Fisheries 1946 *National Farm Survey of England and Wales 1941–1943. A summary report*. HMSO

Ministry of Agriculture, Fisheries and Food 1973 *Agriculture in the urban fringe. A survey of the Slough/Hillingdon area*. Ministry of Agriculture, Fisheries and Food Agricultural Development and Advisory Service (Technical report 30)

Ministry of Agriculture, Fisheries and Food 1976 *EEC survey on the structure of agricultural holdings, 1975: England and Wales*. Press notice

Ministry of Agriculture, Fisheries and Food 1982 *Agricultural statistics United Kingdom 1980 and 1981*. HMSO

Ministry of Agriculture, Fisheries and Food 1987 *Farm Incomes in the United Kingdom: 1987 Edition*. HMSO

Moss J E 1980 *Part-time farming in Northern Ireland. A study of small scale beef and sheep farms*. Department of Agriculture Northern Ireland Economics and Statistics Division (Studies in agricultural economics)

Munton R 1983 *London's green belt: containment in practice*. George Allen and Unwin (The London research series in geography 3)

Munton R J, Whatmore S J, Little J K, Marsden T K 1985 Part-time farming and the rural landscape: some observations on method and preliminary results from the metropolitan green belt. Paper presented to Agricultural Economics Society Conference, London

Nalson J S 1968 *Mobility of farm families. A study of occupational and residential mobility in an upland area of England*. Manchester University Press

National Farmers' Union 1985 Safeguarding the smaller farm: the way forward. An NFU discussion paper. National Farmers' Union

Newby H, Bell C, Rose D, Saunders P 1978 *Property, paternalism and power: class and control in rural England.* Hutchinson University Library

Northfield Lord 1979 Report of the Committee of Inquiry into the acquisition and occupancy of agricultural land. HMSO, Cmnd 7599

Organisation for Economic Co-operation and Development 1978 *Part-time farming in OECD countries: general report.* Organisation for Economic Co-operation and Development, Paris (OECD agricultural policy reports)

Persson L O 1983 Part time farming – corner-stone or obstacle in rural development? *Sociologia Ruralis* xxiii(1): 50–62

Regev C 1980 Part-time farming in Israel. In *The role of agriculture in society.* Papers presented at fourth international farm management congress, Commonwealth Agricultural Bureaux, Slough, pp. 65–8

Rettie W J 1975 Scotland's farm occupiers. *Scottish Agricultural Economics* xxv:387–93

Robson N 1987 The changing role of part-time farming in the structure of agriculture. *Journal of Agricultural Economics* xxxviii(2):168–75

Rural Voice 1985 *Agriculture and the rural economy. A Rural Voice policy statement.* Rural Voice

Sander W 1983 Off-farm employment and income of farmers. *Oxford Agrarian Studies* xii:34–47

Scola P M 1961 Scotland's farms and farmers. *Scottish Agricultural Economics* xi:59–62

Shaw P R 1979 Canadian farm and nonfarm family incomes. *American Journal of Agricultural Economics* 61(3):676–82

Spedding C R W 1981 The role of small-scale farming. In Tranter R B (ed.) *Smallfarming and the nation.* University of Reading Centre for Agricultural Strategy (CAS paper 9)

Symes D G 1982 Part-time farming in Norway. *GeoJournal* 6(4):351–4

Symes D G, Marsden T J 1983 Complementary roles and asymmetrical lives: farmers' wives in a large farm environment. *Sociologia Ruralis* xxiii(3/4):229–41

Thomas E, Elms C E 1938 *An economic survey of Buckinghamshire agriculture: Part I farms and estates.* University of Reading Department of Agricultural Economics (Bulletin 51)

Tracy M 1984 Issues of agricultural policy in a historical framework. *Journal of Agricultural Economics* xxxv(3):307–18

Tubman W 1977 A note on off-farm income of farm families in Australia. *Australian Journal of Agricultural Economics* 21(3):209–14

Wagstaff H R 1970 Scotland's farm occupiers. *Scottish Agricultural Economics* xx:277–85

Wibberley G 1977 Resumé of the seminar. In Gasson R (ed.) *The place of part-time farming in rural and regional development.* Wye College Centre for European Agricultural Studies, pp. 123–8

Wimberley R C 1983 The emergence of part-time farming as a social form of agriculture. In Simpson I H, Simpson R L (eds) *Research in sociology of work: peripheral workers volume 2.* JAI Press, Greenwich, Connecticut, pp. 325–56

Index